FIRST PLACE ❖
Favorites

❖ RECIPES ❖

First Place Materials are published by
LifeWay Press
127 Ninth Avenue North
Nashville, TN 37234

© Copyright 1992 (revised, 1994) Reprinted 1997
ISBN 0-7673-2616-4
Houston's First Baptist Church
7401 Katy Freeway
Houston, TX 77024

Dewey Decimal Classification: 248.4
Subject Heading: Christian Life/Physical Fitness

Printed in the United States of America

Acknowledgements

Unless otherwise indicated, biblical quotations are from the Holy
Bible, *New International Version,* copyright © 1973, 1978, 1984 by
International Bible Society.
Used by permission.

ACKNOWLEDGMENTS

We gratefully acknowledge the contribution of hundreds of *First Place* members and leaders who helped to make *First Place Favorites* possible. Over the years we have collected hundreds of favorite recipes from all over the United States. We give special thanks to the *First Place* leaders at Houston's First Baptist Church who checked each recipe for correct exchange counts. Special thanks also go to Kay Smith for hundreds of hours spent preparing the recipes, making whatever changes were needed, and for coordinating the entire project.

Carole Lewis
National Director, *First Place*

Contents

LIFE-STYLE CHANGES

First Place

Life-style Change

"Therefore glorify God in your body and in your spirit, which are God's." 1 Corinthians 6:20

Such an awesome thought. Do we glorify God in our body, and in our spirit? Do we really do our part to keep our body as fit as possible? God has given us a free will to make choices. Many choices we make in the areas of food and exercise leave us with bodies that do not glorify God and put us at risk for many major health problems.

America leads all other developed countries in the major health diseases: heart disease, hypertension, cancer, diabetes, lower back pain, and stress related diseases. In America, we are very fortunate to have a vast quantity of high quality food choices. Often we choose food with absolutely no nutritional value. Our bodies were not designed for the sedentary life-styles we have adopted. This is an excerpt from Building God's Temple by Dr. Dick Couey on 1 Corinthians 6:20.

Man's option to choose whether he will care for his body and spirit is shown in this verse. God has given man a free will to choose for himself. But He has also given man rules by which to live. God knows that for man to be truly happy he must obey and live his life according to God's directions. Many Christians, who stray from His directions, experience unhappiness for choosing the wrong life-style. We all stray and many of us are still learning to put God first in our life.

2

In this verse God provides the rule that will make us truly happy. He is directing us to glorify God in our bodies to the best of our ability, and to condition our body to optimum physical capability... Good health will enhance our service for Him and we can serve more effectively without stress and fatigue.

Many Christians choose to neglect this directive. They let false pleasures dominate their bodies. Many overeat, eat foods without nutritional value, drink alcohol, smoke tobacco, worry unnecessarily and avoid every opportunity to exercise. This life-style is very prevalent among Christians of all denominations. This is an attitude of negligence of God's directive. Many Christians are obedient to God's spiritual laws; they attend church regularly, tithe accordingly, and serve others with compassion and concern, but do not glorify God in their bodies. This lack of obedience to God's command is sin. I feel it is sin to neglect the physical needs of God's temple.[1]

OBESITY

Obesity in the United States is widespread. Public health records estimate 50 to 66 percent of Americans are over-fat. Forty-six percent of these are considered obese. More than 40% of our school age children are considered over-fat. It is of great importance to keep children lean to avoid overproduction of fat cells. Fat cells can be shrunk in size but the number of fat cells will never decrease.

[1] Couey, Dick, *Building God's Temple* (Minneapolis: Burgess Publishing Company, 1982), 17.

3

This makes it more difficult to stay fit. Medical research has proven obesity drastically increases a person's chances of serious health problems and a shortened life expectancy.

The actual amount of body fat is the important issue. A young mother came into the First Place office one day and asked to have a body composition analysis. To the eye she looked very fit. She was concerned because she was not exercising and revealed her love for "junk food." The composition showed that her body fat was 31%. We jokingly told her she had a fat person inside just waiting to get out. Usually a look in the mirror will reveal the truth. If you look fat - you are fat. Women's body fat content should be between 22%-28%. Men should be between 12%-19%. Millions of dollars are spent annually on weight loss in the United States. Many offer quick weight loss plans, magical gimmicks, pills, etc. Some are complete with testimonies and money-back guarantees. Losing weight too quickly will result also in losing lean body mass along with fat and water. Some of these are dangerous, both physically and mentally.

Christians, if you are truly interested in your total health, plus keeping the weight off, it will mean permanently changing eating habits and activities. The life-style change emphasized in First Place is designed to be forever. Many members will be like the young mother in this story. Her weight was correct but she needed to eat properly and exercise to attain a healthy body. Many will have more than a hundred pounds to lose. The weight loss testimonies in First Place are inspiring. First Place members have proven--weight loss can be permanent. Some members join First Place because they have been diagnosed with heart disease, diabetes, or illnesses which require proper eating. All of these goals can be met in First Place. The food plan recommended is what medical professionals suggest for healthy living. Our goal in First Place is to never "diet." We develop a healthy life-style consisting of healthy food choices and exercise.

GOOD NUTRITION

Scientists are not aware of any one "perfect" food that can supply all the recommended daily allowances. To meet our nutritional needs, we must eat a variety of food. Nutrients in food perform different functions that keep our body operating efficiently. The **major nutrients** are **carbohydrates, proteins, fats, vitamins, minerals,** and **water**. Although fiber is not considered a nutrient, it performs important functions in the nutritional process by providing roughage to keep nutrients and waste moving through the system. Carbohydrates, fats, and protein serve as sources of energy and fuel for performing bodily functions.

PROTEIN is the basic structural substance of each cell in the body. Proteins help to build, maintain, and repair cells.

FATS are a very concentrated source of energy providing more than twice the amount of calories compared with proteins and carbohydrates. Fats transport certain vitamins throughout the body.

VITAMINS are essential to maintain life. The body cannot manufacture vitamins with the exception of vitamin D. Therefore, vitamin needs must be provided by the foods we eat. Vitamins do not provide energy, but they do help the body generate and use energy.

MINERALS also do not furnish the body with energy, but give strength and rigidity to certain body tissues and assist with numerous vital functions. Eating balanced meals will provide daily mineral needs.

WATER, like no other chemical compound, serves the body in many distinct and vital functions. All chemical reaction of metabolism takes place in water.

RECOMMENDED DIETARY GUIDELINES

Health professionals agree that the relationship of overall health and nutrients has been proven. The foods we choose can directly affect our health. The American Dietetic

Association, the American Diabetic Association and the American Heart Association joined forces to publish dietary guidelines to promote a healthier American public. First Place definitely stays within these guidelines. We have printed the eight topics with an explanation of our recommendations in First Place.

1. Calorie intake should be appropriate to reach and maintain a reasonable body weight.

Our bodies require a certain number of calories each day. Extra calories are stored in the body as fat. We recommend no less than 1200 calories for women and no less than 1500 calories for men. The ideal situation would be to know your personal B.M.R., eat that number of calories and with the recommended exercise, weight loss would occur. First Place is not a fast way to lose weight. The goal of First Place is a permanent weight loss through a life-style change. The word "diet" is out. We use the Exchange Plan which is recommended by the American Diabetic and Amercian Dietetic Associations as a healthy way to eat. If healthy eating habits and regular exercise become a part of your life-style, maintaining your weight loss will not be a problem. Eating properly does not have to mean "sparingly." Many will find themselves eating more because healthy choices do not always mean less volume. We do not encourage anyone to eat things they do not like or to be hungry. The beautiful part of the Exchange Plan is that you will be able to find foods you do like and can enjoy eating from each list. If you are truly hungry, you would be advised to go up on the calorie chart to add exchanges. Maintenance in First Place is just more of First Place.

2. Carbohydrate intake should be about 55%. High fiber, complex carbohydrates should be substituted for low fiber, simple carbohydrates.

First Place members are encouraged to choose carbohydrates wisely. Complex carbohydrates are important to our health. We recommend 25 plus grams of fiber per day. We suggest using whole grain products. Whole wheat bread for instance, not just wheat. Check your packaged food products for the amount of fiber per serving. Choose whole grain cereals, dried beans, and whole grain rice to assure your body receives the fiber it needs.

Simple carbohydrates occur naturally in fruits, milk and certain vegetables. All the simple carbohydrates your body needs are supplied through these foods. Therefore, any product with sugar or syrup is not recommended. When you check the ingredients list you will often find words listed that are just different words for sugar such as sorbitol, sucrose, dextrose, and fructose. None of these are recommended in First Place. Shop wisely, read ingredient lists, and become familiar with all words that are different forms of sugar.

3. Protein intake should be limited to 20% of total daily calories.

Proteins help our bodies build and repair body tissue. They regulate fluid balance, help carry fats, minerals, drugs, and other products in the blood. Proteins also make antibodies, enzymes, and hormones. Animal protein is complete because it contains amino acids. We want to choose lean meats and meat products that provide the 7 grams of protein necessary to be classified a meat product.

Proteins found in vegetables are not complete and must be combined correctly to complement each other to provide good quality protein. If a First Place member chooses to combine vegetables, we ask that the member take on the responsibility of checking carefully that the correct combinations are met.

4. Total fat intake should be limited to 25% of total daily. Total dietary cholesterol intake should be less than 300 milligrams a day. Polyunsaturated fats, and especially monounsaturated fats, should be substituted for saturated fats whenever possible.

First Place members receive all the saturated fat their bodies need in their meat exchanges. When choosing the additional fats per day (1 fat per meal on 1200 calorie plan), we recommend choosing a monounsaturated or polyunsaturated fat. Check your packaged products such as margarine to make sure saturated fat is not the primary ingredient. Saturated fat is found in milk, butter, cheese, meats, coconut oil, palm oil, shortening, and chocolate. Our bodies need the fat recommended, but keep in mind, any excess amount of fat our body receives is quickly stored and puts us at risk for many major diseases.

Cholesterol is found in animal fats. It is used in our body to build cells and to make hormones and bile acids. One important fact to learn is our liver makes all the cholesterol our body needs. An excess of cholesterol in your system is a risk factor for heart disease. Another very important fact to learn is that dietary cholesterol is considered by health professionals as a secondary health factor. The most important factor is not to eat an excessive amount of fat, especially saturated fat. Carefully examine packaged foods. Many packaged foods may say "no cholesterol" leading the consumer to believe it is a wise choice. BEWARE: many times these products are loaded with fat, making it a very poor choice for a First Place member.

5. Alternative Sweeteners

Much of the health research on artificial sweeteners is inconclusive. The recommendation of First Place is "moderation." Be aware of the amounts you consume. We have provided a list of sugar equivalents for various brand names not as an endorsement, but for your convenience. This chart is on pages 299-300.

6. Sodium intake should be limited to 3 grams (3,000 milligrams) per day.

The body can function quite normally on 1/10 teaspoon of salt daily which is 0.2 grams. Carefully examine packaged foods for the amount of sodium. The sodium in salt makes the body retain fluid. Fluid retention can lead to raising the blood pressure. Be sure to limit luncheon meats, dill pickles, corned beef, ham, canned foods, and packaged foods containing high amounts of sodium.

7. Alcohol

Alcohol is not a part of the First Place program. It is an irritant to the digestive system. It can lead to acute inflammation of the pancreas, which interferes with the production of insulin and results in diabetes. Alcohol can cause internal bleeding, inflammation, loss of appetite, diarrhea, and vomiting.

Alcohol has been proven to cause negative effects on these body parts: circulatory system, heart, kidneys, liver, and reproductive system. Alcohol has been proven to cause major health problems in babies of mothers who drink while pregnant. Drinking alcohol degrades our Creator in whose image we have been made.

8. A wide variety of food should be consumed.

First Place is not a "diet." By using the exchange list you will be eating a wide variety of food. We encourage each member to plan well-balanced nutritious meals. Eating a variety of foods will supply your body with the basic nutrients needed for a healthy body. Shop wisely and be creative. Eating healthy should be exciting and tasteful.

APPETIZERS

SAUSAGE BALLS

Chol: 21 mg   **Carbo:** 1 gm   **Fat:** 2 gm
Calories: 34   **Protein:** 3 gm   **Fiber:** Tr.
Sodium: 36 mg

INGREDIENTS:
16 oz. turkey breakfast sausage
6 Tbsp. grated Parmesan cheese
2 slices lite bread made into crumbs
2 Tbsp. dried parsley flakes
2 eggs
1/2 tsp. ground red pepper
1/2 C. finely diced celery and onions

STEPS IN PREPARATION:
1. Mix all ingredients together until well blended. Form into individual balls (approx. 1/2 Tbsp. each). Place balls on cookie sheet that has been sprayed with non-stick cooking spray. Freeze.
2. To cook, place balls in 350 degree oven for 12 minutes, then broil for 2 minutes to brown. Yields approximately 40 sausage balls.

BUFFALO WINGS

EACH SERVING Amount: 4 wings
Exchanges: 2 meat
              1 fat

Chol: 68 mg   Carbo: 1 gm   Fat: 8 gm
Calories: 178 Protein: 26 gm Fiber: Tr.
Sodium: 213 mg

INGREDIENTS:

12 chicken wing drummettes
2 Tbsp. melted diet margarine
2 Tbsp. bottled hot sauce
1 1/2 Tbsp. red wine vinegar

STEPS IN PREPARATION:

1. If using wings, remove and discard tips. Cut wings into 2 pieces at the joint.
2. Broil chicken 20-25 minutes.
3. Combine butter, tabasco, and vinegar in saucepan. Add chicken. Toss to coat evenly.

Serves 3

STUFFED APPLES

EACH SERVING Amount: 1 portion
Exchanges: 1 meat
1/2 fruit
1 fat

Chol: 0   **Carbo:** 10 gm **Fat:** 6 gm
Calories: 99 **Protein:** 3 gm **Fiber:** 2 gm
Sodium: 92 mg

INGREDIENTS:
1 apple
1/4 C. corn flakes
6 tsp. chunky peanut butter

STEPS IN PREPARATION:
1. Cut the apple in half and scoop core out of center. Discard core. Carefully use spoon (a grapefruit spoon will work well) to scoop out the inside of the apple.
2. In a bowl, combine the apple, corn flakes and peanut butter. Mix well.
3. Fill each apple shell with the mixture.
Serves 2

SHRIMP (CRAB OR CLAM) STUFFED MUSHROOMS

EACH SERVING Amount: 3 mushrooms
Exchanges: 1 meat
              1/2 bread
              1/2 vegetable

Chol: 13 mg   **Carbo:** 13 gm   **Fat:** 1 gm
Calories: 95   **Protein:** 8 gm   **Fiber:** 2 gm
Sodium: 133 mg

INGREDIENTS:

24 mushrooms
1 onion, chopped
1 (8 oz.) can cooked shrimp, crab or minced clams
1 C. Italian bread crumbs
1/2 tsp. oregano
1/2 tsp. thyme
1/2 tsp. parsley flakes

STEPS IN PREPARATION:

1. Cut stems from mushrooms; chop fine.
2. Coat saucepan with non-stick spray. Add chopped stems and onion, saute for 5 minutes, stirring constantly. Add shrimp (crab or clams), bread crumbs and seasonings. Cook until thoroughly mixed adding water if needed.
3. Stuff mushroom caps with meat mixture; place in baking dish.
4. Bake in pre-heated 350 degree oven for 30 minutes.

Serves 8

FRUITED SQUARES

EACH SERVING Amount: 1 portion
Exchanges: 3/4 fruit
              1/2 fat

Chol: 0   **Carbo:** 11 gm **Fat:** 2 gm
Calories: 72   **Protein:** 1 gm **Fiber:** Tr.
Sodium: 51 mg

INGREDIENTS:

2 pkg. (4 serving) or 1 pkg. (8 serving) sugar-free gelatin, any flavor

1 1/2 C. boiling water

1 C. cold water

Ice cubes

1 C. sugar-free whipped topping

1 C. fruit juice or 2 C. sliced or diced fresh fruit

STEPS IN PREPARATION:

1. Dissolve gelatin in boiling water.
2. Combine cold water and ice cubes to make 2 1/2 cups. Add to gelatin and stir until slightly thickened; remove any unmelted ice.
3. Measure 1 cup and fold into whipped topping; pour into 8 inch square pan. Chill about 10 minutes.
4. Place fruit over creamy layer, then spoon remaining gelatin over fruit. Chill until firm, about 3 hours. Cut into squares.

Serves 8

Suggested Combinations:
Raspberry or strawberry flavor with sliced
pineapple or peaches.
Cherry, Hawaiian pineapple or lime flavor with
sliced pineapple or peaches.
Orange or lemon flavor with apricot halves or
mandarin orange slices.
Any flavor with fruit cocktail.

VEGETABLE CHRISTMAS TREE

EACH SERVING Amount: 1 cup
Exchanges: 1 vegetable

Chol: 0   **Carbo:** 6 gm   **Fat:** Tr.
Calories: 30   **Protein:** 2 gm **Fiber:** 1 gm
Sodium: 20 mg

You will need a 12" to 18" Styrofoam cone. Wrap cone in colored foil or wrapping paper. Use florist putty to secure base to plate.

INGREDIENTS:
1 head broccoli
1 head cauliflower
carrots
cherry tomatoes
radishes
green peppers and red peppers
whatever other vegetables are in season you like

STEPS IN PREPARATION:
1. Cut all vegetables into chunks. Place wooden picks in cut vegetables.
2. Arrange in cone from bottom up. Arrange remainder of vegetables around base in plate.
3. Serve with low-calorie dip.

BEVERAGES

BANANA SHAKE

EACH SERVING Amount: 1 portion
Exchanges: 1 fruit
1/2 milk

Chol: 2 mg   **Carbo:** 35 gm   **Fat:** 1 gm
Calories: 156   **Protein:** 5 gm   **Fiber:** 3 gm
Sodium: 64 mg

INGREDIENTS:
1/2 frozen ripe banana, 3 oz.
5 ice cubes
1/2 C. skim milk
1 pkg. sugar substitute
1/4 tsp. banana flavoring

STEPS IN PREPARATION:
1. Peel ripe banana, cut in half and freeze. Cut the banana into 3 or 4 pieces.
2. Put the ice cubes in blender on lowest speed to chop up the ice. Add the pieces of frozen banana and allow them to be chopped up. Add the milk, flavoring and sugar substitute and blend for a few seconds to mix. Pour in a glass and serve.
3. An alternate method is to put all the ingredients in at one time and blend for a few minutes until the ice and banana are chopped up. Chopping the ice and banana up first makes a little smoother drink.

Serves 1

Variations: Using 2% milk will make a little richer drink and will add 1 fat exchange. Using whole milk adds 2 fat exchanges. If the taste is a little bland, vary the amount of flavoring and sweetener or try using vanilla flavoring. Other frozen fruits such as peaches or strawberries can be used.

BANANA SMOOTHIE

EACH SERVING Amount: 1 portion
Exchanges: 1 fruit
1 milk

Chol: 9 mg   Carbo: 49 gm Fat: 1 gm
Calories: 165 Protein: 16 gm Fiber: 3 gm
Sodium: 242 mg

INGREDIENTS:
1/3 C. non-fat dry powdered milk
2 tsp. cocoa
1/2 banana, mashed
1 C. water
3-4 ice cubes

STEPS IN PREPARATION:
1. Mix in blender. Pour into glass.
2. You can vary the recipe with different fruits (3/4 C. strawberries, blueberries, etc.), and add flavoring as desired. You also can freeze this recipe to eat rather than drink.

Serves 1

TROPICAL SMOOTHIE

EACH SERVING Amount: 1 portion
Exchanges: 1 fruit
                1/4 milk

Chol: 0   Carbo: 41 gm Fat: 1 gm
Calories: 155 Protein: 4 gm Fiber: 4 gm
Sodium: 42 mg

INGREDIENTS:

1/4 C. non-fat yogurt
1/4 C. canned crushed pineapple, drained (in its own juice)
1 1/2 oz. banana, peeled and sliced
1 pkg. sugar substitute
1/4 C. cracked ice

STEPS IN PREPARATION:

Put all ingredients into a blender and blend until smooth.
Serves 1

BLUEBERRY THICK SHAKE

EACH SERVING Amount: 1 portion
Exchanges: 1 meat
1 fruit
1/2 milk

Chol: 21 mg   Carbo: 16 gm   Fat: 5 gm
Calories: 161   Protein: 5 gm   Fiber: 2 gm
Sodium: 148 mg

INGREDIENTS:
1/2 C. skim milk
2 oz. part-skim ricotta cheese
1/3 C. blueberries (fresh or frozen with no sugar
added)
1/2 tsp. vanilla
sugar substitute

STEPS IN PREPARATION:
1. In blender, on high speed, blend ricotta, milk
and vanilla until smooth. Add blueberries and
sugar substitute to taste; blend until almost
smooth.
2. Serve at once.
Serves 1

ORANGE DELIGHT

INGREDIENTS:
1/4 C. orange juice
1/2 C. skim milk
1/4 C. pineapple in its own juice (crushed)
1 or 2 pkg. sugar substitute
1/2 tsp. orange extract

STEPS IN PREPARATION:
Mix all and freeze. After frozen, put in blender.
Serves 1

GEL DELIGHT

EACH SERVING Amount: 1 portion
Exchanges: 1 milk
              1 fruit, if added

Chol: 4 mg   Carbo: 12 gm Fat: 0
Calories: 86 Protein: 8 gm Fiber: 0
Sodium: 126 mg

INGREDIENTS:

1 small pkg. any flavor sugar-free gelatin
1 C. low-fat skim milk

STEPS IN PREPARATION:

1. Make and gel one small package of any flavor sugar-free gelatin.
2. Combine 1/2 cup of set gelatin with 1 cup of low-fat skim milk in blender. Blend until smooth.
3. Frozen fruit may be added if desired. Count 1 fruit per 1/2 cup added.

Serves 1

GELATIN SPARKLE

EACH SERVING Amount: 1 portion
Exchanges: free

Chol: 0   **Carbo:** 0   **Fat:** 0
Calories: 9   **Protein:** 1 gm   **Fiber:** 0
Sodium: 59 mg

INGREDIENTS:
1 small pkg. sugar-free gelatin, any flavor
1 C. boiling water
1 C. cold diet carbonated beverage

STEPS IN PREPARATION:
Dissolve gelatin in boiling water. Add beverage and chill in individual glasses until set, about 2 hours.
Serves 4

Suggested Combinations:
Lime, mixed fruit or Hawaiian-pineapple with
    diet ginger ale.
Orange flavor with diet root beer.
Cherry or lemon flavor with diet cola.
Strawberry, triple berry or lime flavor with diet
    lemon-lime carbonated beverage.

PINEAPPLE SHAKER SNACK

EACH SERVING Amount: 1/2 cup
Exchanges: 1/2 bread
1/2 fruit
1/2 milk

Chol: 3 mg   **Carbo:** 27 gm   **Fat:** 0
Calories: 135   **Protein:** 7 gm   **Fiber:** 1 gm
Sodium: 131 mg

INGREDIENTS:

2 C. cold low-fat milk
1 small pkg. sugar-free vanilla instant pudding
1 1/2 C. canned crushed pineapple, in juice

STEPS IN PREPARATION:

1. Pour milk into a leakproof 1 1/2-quart container. Add mix and crushed pineapple. Cover tightly; shake vigorously at least 45 seconds. Pour at once into dishes.
2. Pudding will be softset in 5 minutes.

Serves 4

CHERRY BERRY FLING

EACH SERVING Amount: 1 portion
Exchanges: 1/2 fruit

Chol: 0   Carbo: 13 gm Fat: 0
Calories: 53   Protein: 0   Fiber: 2 gm
Sodium: 3 mg

INGREDIENTS:
1 (16 oz.) pkg. frozen unsweetened strawberries
1 (6 oz.) can undiluted unsweetened frozen pink
   lemonade
3 (12 oz.) diet cherry lemon-lime soda

STEPS IN PREPARATION:
Combine berries, lemonade, and soda in blender
and add enough ice cubes to fill. Mix until smooth.
Serves 4

CRANBERRY WARMER

EACH SERVING Amount: 1 portion
Exchanges: 3/4 fruit

Chol: 0   **Carbo:** 11 gm   **Fat:** 0
Calories: 43   **Protein:** 0   **Fiber:** 0
Sodium: 4 mg

INGREDIENTS:

4 C. cranberry juice cocktail, low calorie
1 (18 oz.) can unsweetened pineapple juice
1 tsp. whole allspice
1 tsp. whole cloves
dash salt
dash ground nutmeg
3" stick cinnamon

STEPS IN PREPARATION:

1. In saucepan combine all ingredients; slowly bring mixture to boil. Reduce heat; cover and simmer 20 minutes. Remove from heat.
2. Strain to remove spices.

Serves 12

WASSAIL

EACH SERVING Amount: 1/2 cup
Exchanges: 1/2 fruit

Chol: 0 **Carbo:** 7 gm **Fat:** 0
Calories: 27 **Protein:** 0 **Fiber:** 0
Sodium: 3 mg

Mix equal parts apple juice and cranberry juice. Add cinnamon, nutmeg and cloves to taste. Heat and serve with a cinnamon stick.

HOLIDAY CRANBERRY PUNCH

INGREDIENTS:

4 C. cranberries
1 quart unsweetened apple juice
1 quart water
1 Tbsp. grated orange rind
6 - 3" cinnamon sticks
12 whole cloves
1 quart unsweetened orange juice

STEPS IN PREPARATION:

1. Place orange rind, cinnamon sticks, and cloves in a cheese cloth bag.
2. In pan add all remaining ingredients except the orange juice. Bring to a boil for 5 minutes or until the cranberries burst.
3. Strain, add orange juice and serve. Reheat if necessary.

Serves 22

TOMATO JUICE COCKTAIL

EACH SERVING **Amount:** 1 portion
Exchanges: 1/4 fruit

Chol: 0   **Carbo:** 5 gm   **Fat:** 0
Calories: 30   **Protein:** 2 gm **Fiber:** 1 gm
Sodium: 552 mg

INGREDIENTS:

1 small pkg. lemon or orange flavor sugar-free
    gelatin
1/2 tsp. salt
3/4 C. boiling tomato juice
1 C. cold tomato juice
1 Tbsp. lemon juice
1 tsp. prepared horseradish

STEPS IN PREPARATION:

1. Dissolve gelatin and salt in boiling tomato juice. Add remaining ingredients and pour into 8x4 inch loaf pan.
2. Chill until firm, about 4 hours.
3. Cut into 1 inch cubes and serve in individual glasses.

Serves 4

BREADS

CORNBREAD

EACH SERVING Amount: 1 portion
Exchanges: 2 meats
                  1 bread
                  1/2 milk
                  1/2 fat

Chol: 225 mg **Carbo:** 11 gm **Fat:** 7 gm
Calories: 183 **Protein:** 18 gm **Fiber:** 2 gm
Sodium: 1174 mg

INGREDIENTS:

4 oz. skim milk

1 oz. cornmeal (2 Tbsp.)

1/4 tsp. salt

1 egg, separated

1 oz. grated low-fat cheddar cheese

STEPS IN PREPARATION:

1. Over low heat, cook milk, cornmeal and salt until the mixture thickens. Stir in beaten egg yolk and cheese.
2. Beat egg white until stiff and fold in. Place in muffin tins that have been sprayed with non-stick spray.
3. Bake at 375 degrees for 30 minutes.

Makes a good lunch with salad and fruit.
Serves 1

FAT-FREE CORN BREAD

EACH SERVING Amount: 1 portion
Exchanges: 1 bread

Chol: 1 mg   **Carbo:** 15 gm   **Fat:** Tr.
Calories: 77   **Protein:** 3 gm   **Fiber:** 3 gm
Sodium: 391 mg

INGREDIENTS:
1 1/4 C. cornmeal
1/3 C. whole wheat flour
1 tsp. baking powder
1 tsp. baking soda
1/2 tsp. salt
1/2 C. grated carrots
1 Tbsp. apple juice concentrate
1 C. non-fat buttermilk
2 egg whites (discard yolks)

STEPS IN PREPARATION:
1. Preheat oven to 350 degrees.
2. Use an 8" square non-stick pan, or a regular pan coated with a non-stick cooking spray.
3. In a medium bowl, combine cornmeal, flour, baking powder, baking soda.
4. In a small bowl, beat egg whites until foamy. Mix salt, carrots, apple juice, and buttermilk. Add to this mixture the flour mixture and then the egg whites. Blend thoroughly.
5. Pour into pan and bake for 20-25 minutes, or until springy to the touch.

Serves 8

QUICK BREAD STICKS

EACH SERVING Amount: 5 sticks
Exchanges: 1 bread
                1/2 fat

Chol: 1 mg   Carbo: 23 gm   Fat: 7 gm
Calories: 139 Protein: 4 gm Fiber: 0
Sodium: 417 mg

INGREDIENTS:

1 (10 count) can low-fat refrigerated biscuits
11/4 C. rice cereal, coarsely crushed
1/2 tsp. salt
3 Tbsp. skim milk
11/2 Tbsp. grated Parmesan cheese

STEPS IN PREPARATION:
1. Cut each biscuit into thirds. Roll each piece into a 4 inch stick.
2. Combine cereal and salt. Roll each stick in milk and then in cereal. Place on baking sheet and sprinkle with cheese.
3. Bake at 400 degrees for 8 to 10 minutes or until golden brown.

Serves 6

If flaky large biscuits are used, 4 sticks =
                1 bread
                1/2 fat

CHEESE BREAD

INGREDIENTS:

1 medium egg
1 Tbsp. dehydrated onion flakes
1 oz. low-fat sharp cheddar cheese, diced
1/2 C. skim milk
1 slice lite bread, crumbled

STEPS IN PREPARATION:

Mix all ingredients and bake in an 8 oz. baking dish at 350 degrees until golden brown (for about 15 minutes).
Serves 1

TURKEY DRESSING

EACH SERVING Amount: 1 portion
Exchanges: 1/4 meat
11/2 bread
1/4 milk
1/2 vegetable
3/4 fat

Chol: 56 mg Carbo: 23 gm Fat: 7 gm
Calories: 194 Protein: 10 gm Fiber: 4 gm
Sodium: 938 mg

INGREDIENTS:
11/2 C. white cornmeal
2 Tbsp. all purpose flour
1 pkg. sugar substitute
1 tsp. baking powder
1/4 tsp. salt
11/4 C. low-fat buttermilk
2 eggs, beaten
2 Tbsp. vegetable oil
1 C. celery, diced
1 C. onions, grated
31/4 C. chicken broth, divided
11/4 C. herb flavored stuffing mix
1 tsp. rubbed sage
1 tsp. white pepper
1/2 tsp. garlic powder

STEPS IN PREPARATION:
1. Combine cornmeal, flour, sugar substitute, baking powder, and salt in a large mixing bowl; add buttermilk, eggs, and oil; mix well.
2. Place 1 Tbsp. vegetable oil in a 10-inch cast iron skillet. Place skillet in 450 degree oven for

3-4 minutes or until hot. Tilt pan to evenly distribute oil; pour batter into pan.
3. Bake at 350 degrees for 25 minutes. Cool; crumble the cornbread into a large bowl.
4. Cook celery and onion in 1/2 C. broth in a skillet until tender. Add celery mixture, remaining broth (adjusting moisture to desired consistency) and remaining ingredients to cornbread crumbs; mix well.
5. Spoon mixture into a 12 x 8 x 2 baking dish sprayed with non-stick spray. Bake dressing at 350 degrees for 40 minutes.

Serves 8

SLIM JIM STUFFING

EACH SERVING Amount: 1 portion
Exchanges: 1 bread
1/3 vegetable
1/2 fat

Chol: Tr. **Carbo:** 14 gm **Fat:** 6 gm
Calories: 110 **Protein:** 5 gm **Fiber:** 4 gm
Sodium: 857 mg

INGREDIENTS:
1/2 C. minced onion
3/4 C. chopped celery
1/4 C. diet margarine
1/4 C. chicken bouillon
41/2 C. soft bread cubes (use lite bread)
1 tsp. salt
3/4 tsp. sage
1/2 tsp. thyme
1/4 tsp. pepper

STEPS IN PREPARATION:
1. In large skillet, cook and stir onion and celery in margarine until tender. Add chicken bouillon and 1/3 of the bread cubes. Stir. Turn into deep bowl. Add remaining ingredients and toss.
2. Cook in casserole dish that has been sprayed with non-stick cooking spray for 30-35 minutes at 350 degrees.

Serves 6.

WHOLE WHEAT FRUIT BREAD

EACH SERVING Amount: 1 Slice
Exchanges: 1 bread
1/4 vegetable
11/2 fruit

Chol: Tr.   **Carbo:** 42 gm   **Fat:** 1 gm
Calories: 177 **Protein:** 4 gm   **Fiber:** 4 gm
Sodium: 75 mg

INGREDIENTS:
1 C. raisins (golden)
2 C. other dried fruit
3 C. grated carrots
1 C. white flour
1 tsp. baking powder
1 tsp. baking soda
3 tsp. cinnamon
3 C. whole wheat flour
12 oz. frozen, brown apple juice, thawed
(unsweetened)
4 oz. 1/2 % milk

STEPS IN PREPARATION:
1. By hand mix all ingredients above except juice and milk. Add juice and milk and mix.
2. Put thick dough in 2 loaf pans sprayed with non-stick spray.
3. Bake at 325 degrees for 1 hour.
Serves 20

BRAN-FRUIT MUFFINS

EACH SERVING Amount: 2 muffins
Exchanges: 1/2 fruit
              1 1/2 bread
              3/4 fat

Chol: 18 mg   Carbo: 28 gm   Fat: 8 gm
Calories: 213 Protein: 6 gm Fiber: 9 gm
Sodium: 388 mg

INGREDIENTS:

1 C. All-Bran cereal

1/3 C. raisins

1 1/4 C. skim milk

3 Tbsp. vegetable oil

1 egg

1 C. whole wheat flour

1 Tbsp. baking powder

STEPS IN PREPARATION:

1. Preheat oven to 400 degrees and prepare 12-cup muffin pan; lightly grease or spray with non-stick spray or line with paper baking cups.

2. Mix bran cereal and fruit in mixing bowl. Add milk, stir and let stand several minutes. Add oil and egg, beat well.

3. Mix flour and baking powder. Add to bran mixture. Stir until flour is just blended or moistened. Spoon mixture into 12 muffin cups. Immediately place in oven.

4. Bake 15 minutes. Remove from pan immediately.

Serves 6

PUMPKIN MUFFINS

EACH SERVING **Amount:** 3 muffins
Exchanges: 1/2 meat
1 bread
1/4 vegetable
1/2 fruit
1/2 milk

Chol: 37 mg   **Carbo:** 4 gm   **Fat:** 1 gm
Calories: 70   **Protein:** 4 gm   **Fiber:** 1 gm
Sodium: 118 mg

INGREDIENTS:

1 C. pumpkin
2 eggs, beaten
2/3 C. non-fat dry powdered milk
2 tsp. pumpkin spice
1 tsp. cinnamon
6 pkg. sugar substitute
1/2 C. grated carrots
6 Tbsp. flour
4 Tbsp. raisins
1 tsp. baking soda
1 tsp. vanilla

STEPS IN PREPARATION:

1. Combine all dry ingredients in bowl, add eggs and vanilla, then add pumpkin, raisins and carrots. Mix well.
2. Spray a 12-cup muffin pan with non-stick cooking spray. Put mixture into muffin pan.
3. Bake at 350 degrees for 15 minutes.

Serves 4

SOUPS

CHEESE SOUP

EACH SERVING Amount: 3/4 cup
Exchanges: 2 meat
            1/4 bread
            1/4 milk
            1 fat

Chol: 21 mg   Carbo: 1 gm   Fat: 5 gm
Calories: 149   Protein: 16 gm   Fiber: 0
Sodium: 867 mg

INGREDIENTS:

2 (14 1/2 oz.) cans chicken broth
2 C. skim milk
1 lb. grated low-fat American cheese
4 Tbsp. cornstarch
1/4 C. thinly sliced carrots
1/4 C. chopped celery
1/4 C. chopped onion
1 Tbsp. diet margarine

STEPS IN PREPARATION:

1. Heat broth and milk slowly in large pot. Stir grated cheese into broth until melted. (Remove from heat if you can't keep stirring.)
2. Mix cornstarch with as much water as needed to make it pourable. Pour cornstarch mixture slowly into pot.
3. Saute vegetables in margarine. Add to soup.
Serves 8

Variations: Add 1/2 cup chopped cooked broccoli or cauliflower to each cup of soup. Count as 1 vegetable exchange.

CHEDDAR CHEESE SOUP

EACH SERVING Amount: 1 portion
Exchanges: 1/2 lean meat
1/4 bread
1/2 milk
1 1/2 fat

Chol: 21 mg **Carbo:** 22 gm **Fat:** 6 gm
Calories: 219 **Protein:** 20 gm **Fiber:** 0
Sodium: 877 mg

INGREDIENTS:

1/2 C. finely chopped carrots
1 C. finely chopped celery
1 C. finely chopped green onions
2 C. water
1 medium white onion, chopped
2 Tbsp. diet margarine
1 C. flour
4 C. skim or 1/2 % milk
4 C. chicken broth
1 (15 oz.) jar Cheez Whiz, light
salt and pepper to taste
1/4 tsp. cayenne pepper
1 Tbsp. prepared mustard

STEPS IN PREPARATION:

1. Boil carrots, celery and green onions in water 5 minutes.
2. Saute white onion in butter. Add flour and blend well.
3. Boil milk and chicken broth. Stir briskly into white onion mixture with a wire whisk. Add Cheez Whiz, salt, pepper, and cayenne. Stir in

mustard and the boiled vegetables including the water in which they were cooked. Bring to a boil and serve immediately.

4. We do not recommend chopping these ingredients in a food processor.

Serves 16

CREAM OF BROCCOLI SOUP

EACH SERVING Amount: 1 portion
Exchanges: 1 vegetable
1/2 milk
1/2 fat

Chol: 2 mg   **Carbo:** 17 gm **Fat:** 4 gm
Calories: 119 **Protein:** 7 gm **Fiber:** 4 gm
Sodium: 211 mg

INGREDIENTS:

2 Tbsp. diet margarine
1 C. chopped onion
2 1/2 Tbsp. flour
1/2 tsp. salt
1/2 tsp. pepper (or less)
2 C. non-fat chicken broth
10 oz. frozen chopped broccoli, thawed, drained
2 C. skim milk

STEPS IN PREPARATION:

1. Saute onion in margarine, medium heat, about 10 minutes. Add flour, salt and pepper and stir constantly for 2 minutes. Add broth slowly. Add broccoli. Bring to boil, stirring frequently. Cover and simmer until broccoli is tender.
2. Puree in blender.
3. Return to pan, add milk, and bring to simmer.

Serves 4

FRENCH ONION SOUP

EACH SERVING Amount: 1 portion
Exchanges: 1 vegetable
                  1/2 fat

Chol: 1 mg   **Carbo:** 7 gm   **Fat:** 4 gm
Calories: 64   **Protein:** 2 gm   **Fiber:** 1 gm
Sodium: 108 mg

INGREDIENTS:

2 C. onion, sliced
2 Tbsp. diet margarine
4 C. beef broth
1 tsp. Worcestershire sauce
Dash Parmesan Cheese
Croutons, optional (1/3 C. = 1/2 bread, 1/2 fat)

STEPS IN PREPARATION:

1. Saute onions in margarine till lightly browned. Add broth and Worcestershire sauce. Heat until mix comes to a boil.
2. Serve with Parmesan and croutons.

Serves 4

QUICKIE VEGETABLE SOUP

EACH SERVING Amount: 3/4 cup
Exchanges: 1 vegetable

Chol: 0   **Carbo:** 8 gm   **Fat:** 0
Calories: 37   **Protein:** 1 gm   **Fiber:** 3 gm
Sodium: 515 mg

INGREDIENTS:

1 (12 oz.) can V-8 juice, regular or spicy
1 C. water
1/2 chopped onion
2 ribs celery
1 sliced carrot
1 (16 oz.) can green beans
Anything from the list of vegetable exchanges
    (cabbage, etc.)

STEPS IN PREPARATION:

Combine and simmer for about one hour.
Serves 6

TORTILLA SOUP

EACH SERVING Amount: 1 portion
Exchanges: 1/2 meat
                   1 bread
                   1 1/2 vegetable
                   1 fat

Chol: 28   **Carbo:** 25 gm **Fat:** 6 gm
Calories: 214 **Protein:** 12 gm **Fiber:** 5 gm
Sodium: 504 mg

INGREDIENTS:

1/2 C. chopped onion
1/2 C. chopped green peppers
2 cloves garlic, minced
1 Tbsp. vegetable oil
1 (14 1/2 oz.) can tomatoes
1 small can green chiles
1/2 C. picante
1 (10 1/2 oz.) can beef bouillon
1 (10 3/4 oz.) can chicken bouillon
1 (10 1/2 oz.) can tomato juice
1 1/2 C. water
1 tsp. ground cumin
1 C. sliced zucchini
6 corn tortillas cut into 1/2" strips
1/2 C. shredded low-fat cheese

Optional: 3 oz. chicken breast, cubed 1"

STEPS IN PREPARATION:

1. Saute onions, green peppers and garlic in oil in a large Dutch oven until tender; add next 9 ingredients and chicken, optional. Bring to a boil; cover, reduce heat, and simmer 1 hour.

2. Add tortillas and simmer 5 minutes. Top with cheese in bowls.
Serves 6

CABBAGE SOUP

EACH SERVING Amount: 1/2 cup
Exchanges: 1 vegetable

Chol: 0   **Carbo:** 7 gm   **Fat:** 0
Calories: 36   **Protein:** 2 gm   **Fiber:** 2 gm
Sodium: 378 mg

INGREDIENTS:

1 1/2 C. tomato juice
3 C. shredded cabbage
1/2 C. onion flakes (or 1 medium onion, chopped)
Dash of garlic salt and chili powder
2 C. water
1/2 C. diced celery
1 tsp. parsley
1 tsp. bouillon
Salt and pepper to taste
1 (16 oz.) can French-style green beans
1 (16 oz.) can sliced mushrooms

STEPS IN PREPARATION:

Cook all ingredients together except green beans and mushrooms until cabbage is tender. Then add green beans and mushrooms with liquid. Serves 8

CHILI SOUP

EACH SERVING Amount: 1 cup
Exchanges: 11/2 meat
              3/4 bread
              1/2 vegetable
              3/4 fat

Chol: 26 mg   Carbo: 11 gm Fat: 6 gm
Calories: 153 Protein: 10 gm Fiber: 3 gm
Sodium: 64 mg

INGREDIENTS:

1 1/2 lbs. lean ground beef

1 medium onion, chopped

3 (10 3/4 oz.) cans Campbell's condensed
    minestrone soup

1 (14 1/2 oz.) can stewed tomatoes

1 (10 oz.) can Rotell tomatoes

1 (15 1/2 oz.) can chili beans

3 (10 3/4 oz.) cans water

STEPS IN PREPARATION:

Brown together ground beef and chopped onion.
Drain thoroughly. Add remaining ingredients. Mix
together. Simmer for 10 minutes.
Serves 16

EGG & CHEESE

CHICKEN - BROCCOLI - CHEESE AND RICE

EACH SERVING Amount: 1 portion
Exchanges: 3 1/2 meat
1/2 bread
1 vegetable
1 fat

Chol: 49 mg   **Carbo:** 29 gm   **Fat:** 5 gm
Calories: 280   **Protein:** 26 gm   **Fiber:** 8 gm
Sodium: 1154 mg

INGREDIENTS:

12 oz. cooked chicken, cut up (about 4 large
breast halves)
6 oz. Velveeta lite cheese
2 oz. grated low-fat natural cheese
3/4 C. cooked brown rice
2 1/2 C. chicken broth
2/3 C. chopped celery
1 bay leaf
1/2 C. chopped onion
1/3 C. chopped green pepper
20 oz. fresh or frozen chopped broccoli
1/3 C. chicken broth (or water)
1 C. sliced fresh mushrooms (or 4 oz. can)
1 Tbsp. chopped pimiento, optional
1/2 tsp. basil
salt and pepper as desired
1/2 tsp. curry powder, if desired

STEPS IN PREPARATION:

1. Remove skin and fat from chicken. Boil with
   celery leaves, onion, bay leaf.
2. Skim fat off broth and use to cook rice, reserving 1/3 C. for sauteing vegetables. Cook rice

in broth. Add Velveeta, stir to melt.
3. Steam vegetables in broth until slightly tender.
4. Combine all ingredients except grated cheese.
   Pour in casserole and bake at 350 degrees
   until hot and bubbly. Top with grated cheese.
Serves 6

THREE CHEESE CHICKEN BAKE

EACH SERVING Amount: 1 portion
Exchanges: 2 lean meat
                      1 1/2 bread
                      1/2 vegetable
                      1 fat

Chol: 28 mg   **Carbo:** 23 gm **Fat:** 8 gm
Calories: 251 **Protein:** 19 gm **Fiber:** 2 gm
Sodium: 779 mg

INGREDIENTS:

8 oz. lasagna noodles
1/2 C. chopped onion
1/2 C. chopped green pepper
3 Tbsp. diet margarine
1 (10 3/4 oz.) can condensed cream of chicken
    soup
1 (4 oz.) can sliced mushrooms, drained
1/2 C. chopped pimiento
1/3 C. skim milk
1/2 tsp. basil
1 1/2 C. cream-style lite cottage cheese
2 C. (10 oz.) cooked chicken or turkey
1 1/2 C. shredded low-fat American Cheese
          (6 oz.)
1/2 C. grated Parmesan cheese
1 tsp. chili powder, optional

STEPS IN PREPARATION:

1. Cook lasagna noodles in boiling, salted water according to package directions. Drain well.
2. Cook onion and green pepper in diet margarine until tender. Stir in condensed soup, mushrooms, pimiento, skim milk and basil.

3. Lay half the noodles in 13 x 9 x 2 dish. Top with half each chicken, cheeses, and soup mixture. Repeat process.
4. Bake at 350 for 45 minutes. Top with remaining American and Parmesan cheese. Bake 2 minutes more or till cheese melts.

Serves 10

HEARTY MACARONI & CHEESE

EACH SERVING Amount: 1 portion
Exchanges: 1 meat
                  1 bread
                  1/2 milk
                  1 fat

Chol: 93 mg   **Carbo:** 24 gm   **Fat:** 8 gm
Calories: 223 **Protein:** 13 gm **Fiber:** 1 gm
Sodium: 581 mg

INGREDIENTS:

7 oz. elbow macaroni, boiled in salted water and drained
4 eggs
6 oz. shredded low-fat cheese
White Sauce
7 1/2 Tbsp. flour (1/2 C. minus 1/2 tsp.)
7 1/2 Tbsp. diet margarine
3/4 slightly rounded tsp. salt
1/4 to 3/8 tsp. pepper
3 3/4 C. non-fat skim milk

STEPS IN PREPARATION:

1. Boil macaroni.
2. Make white sauce in 2 qt. sauce pan. Add cheese to melt.
3. Beat eggs slighty in a bowl.
4. Add eggs and macaroni to sauce-cheese mixture, stirring as you add. Pour into 13x9 pan sprayed with non-stick spray. Sprinkle with paprika.
5. Bake at 350 degrees for 40-50 minutes until golden brown on top. Serve hot from oven.

Serves 10

BROCCOLI RICE QUICHE

EACH SERVING Amount: 1 portion
Exchanges: 2 meat
               1 bread
               1 vegetable
               1 fat

Chol: 223 mg **Carbo:** 36 gm **Fat:** 8 gm
Calories: 287 **Protein:** 19 gm **Fiber:** 3 gm
Sodium: 1006 mg

INGREDIENTS:

3 C. hot cooked rice (from 1 C. uncooked)
6 oz. grated low-fat cheddar cheese
6 eggs
1 tsp. salt
1/2 C. chopped onions
1 (10 oz.) pkg. frozen chopped broccoli
1/2 C. skim milk
1/4 tsp. pepper
1 (4 oz.) can sliced mushrooms, drained

STEPS IN PREPARATION:

1. Combine rice, 3/4 C. of the cheese, 2 slightly beaten eggs and 1/2 tsp. salt. Press firmly and evenly over bottom and sides of a greased 12" pizza pan or 2-9" pie pans. Set aside.
2. Add onions to broccoli and cook according to package directions. Drain well.
3. Beat remaining eggs slightly. Stir in milk, pepper, mushrooms and remaining salt. Add to broccoli and mix well. Spoon into crust.
4. Bake at 375 degrees for 20 minutes. Sprinkle with remaining cheese. Bake 10 minutes longer. Cool a few minutes before cutting wedges.

Serves 6

IMPOSSIBLE HAM AND BROCCOLI PIE

EACH SERVING Amount: 1 portion
Exchanges: 2 meat
1/4 bread
1/2 vegetable
1/2 fat

Chol: 78 mg **Carbo:** 9 gm **Fat:** 8 gm
Calories: 172 **Protein:** 15 gm **Fiber:** 1 gm
Sodium: 820 mg

INGREDIENTS:
1 1/2 C. frozen broccoli, thawed
1/2 C. low-fat cottage cheese
3 Tbsp. Parmesan cheese
8 oz. full cooked (center slice) ham, lean
1 Tbsp. chopped dried onion, or 3 Tbsp. fresh
chopped onion
1/2 tsp. salt
1/4 tsp. pepper (or cayenne)
4 oz. low-fat cheese, grated
1 C. skim or non-fat milk, minus 2 Tbsp.
2 oz. (scant 1/2 C.) Buttermilk Baking Mix
2 eggs

STEPS IN PREPARATION:
1. Chop ham, add onion, salt, pepper.
2. Layer on bottom of 13 x 9 pan the cottage cheese and Parmesan. Next layer the broccoli, ham, onion, salt and pepper. Top with half the cheese.
3. Beat milk, baking mix, and eggs. Pour over the top.
4. Bake at 350 degrees for 35-40 minutes until knife inserted in center comes out clean.

Serves 8

CRUSTLESS SWISS CHEESE AND ONION QUICHE

EACH SERVING Amount: 1 slice
Exchanges: 1 meat
              1/2 vegetable
              1/2 milk
              1 fat

Chol: 79 mg   Carbo: 13 gm   Fat: 8 gm
Calories: 165   Protein: 12 gm Fiber: 1 gm
Sodium: 846 mg

INGREDIENTS:
4 Tbsp. (3/4 stick) diet margarine
2 medium yellow onions, peeled and sliced
2 eggs, lightly beaten
2 egg whites
1 C. (about 4 oz.) shredded low-fat Swiss cheese
1 1/2 C. canned skim milk
1/8 tsp. ground nutmeg
1 tsp. salt
1/4 tsp. black pepper
1/2 C. fine dry bread crumbs

STEPS IN PREPARATION:
1. Preheat oven to 350 degrees.
2. In a 1 quart saucepan, melt 3 tablespoons of the margarine over moderately low heat. Add onions and cook, covered, for 10 minutes, or until very soft.
3. Meanwhile, in a bowl combine eggs, egg whites, cheese, milk, nutmeg, salt and pepper.
4. When the onions are cooked, spread them out in a 9-inch pie plate that has been sprayed with non-stick spray.

5. Melt the remaining 1 tablespoon of margarine in the saucepan. Pour the egg mixture over the onions and sprinkle the bread crumbs and melted margarine over the top.
6. Bake, uncovered for 30 minutes, or until puffed and set.

Serves 6

CHEESE-STUFFED CHICKEN

EACH SERVING Amount: 1 portion
Exchanges: 3 lean meat
1 fat

Chol: 65 mg **Carbo:** 3 gm **Fat:** 10 gm
Calories: 218 **Protein:** 20 gm **Fiber:** Tr.
Sodium: 502 mg

INGREDIENTS:

4 (3 oz.) whole cooked chicken breasts, skinned, split, and boned
4 (1/2 oz.) slices monterrey jack cheese
2 egg whites
2 tsp. grated parmesan cheese
1 tsp. snipped parsley
1/2 tsp. instant chicken bouillon granules
2 Tbsp. all-purpose flour
1 Tbsp. cooking oil

STEPS IN PREPARATION:

1. In the thickest side of each chicken piece, cut a pocket just large enough for cheese slice. Place a cheese slice in each pocket.
2. Beat together egg whites, Parmesan cheese, parsley, bouillon granules, and dash pepper.
3. Coat chicken with flour and dip in egg mixture.
4. Spray pan with non-stick spray and brown 2 to 3 minutes on each side. Transfer to 10 x 6 x 2 inch baking dish.
5. Bake in 375 degree oven 8 to 10 minutes.
Serves 4

MAIN DISHES

FIRST PLACE PIZZA

EACH SERVING Amount: 1 piece
Exchanges: 2 meat
              1/2 bread

Chol: 65 mg   Carbo: 9 gm   Fat: 8 gm
Calories: 181 Protein: 15 gm Fiber: 2 gm
Sodium: 402 mg

INGREDIENTS:
1 (4 oz.) can chopped mushrooms
1 C. soft bread crumbs, (2 slices whole wheat)
1 egg
1/2 tsp. salt
dash pepper
1 lb. ground chuck
1/2 tsp. oregano
2 oz. low-fat mozzarella cheese
1 (5 1/2 oz.) can pizza sauce
1/4 C. chopped onion
1/4 C. green pepper

STEPS IN PREPARATION:
1. Drain mushrooms, reserve liquid, add water if necessary to equal 1/2 C. Add bread crumbs, egg (slightly beaten), salt and pepper. Let stand 5 minutes. Add ground chuck, 1/2 tsp. oregano, half mushrooms, mix lightly.
2. In 9" pie plate, form a meat crust.
3. Cut 2 slices cheese in 8 triangles, layer over meat. Top with pizza sauce, onion, green pepper and remaining mushrooms. Sprinkle with extra oregano, if desired.
4. Bake at 350 degrees for 55 minutes. Top with remaining cheese; bake 5 minutes. Let stand 10 minutes before serving.

Serves 8

BEEF STEW

EACH SERVING Amount: 11/4 cups
Exchanges: 2 meat
             1/2 bread
             2 vegetable

Chol: 68 mg   Carbo: 17 gm Fat: 5 gm
Calories: 182 Protein: 18 gm Fiber: 2 gm
Sodium: 584 mg

INGREDIENTS:

1 lb. top round, cubed
1Tbsp. cornstarch
1/2 tsp. salt
pepper
1 bouillon cube
1 (16 oz.) can stewed tomatoes
1/4 lb. fresh mushrooms
2 stalks celery, chopped
1 med. onion, chopped
1 large potato, peeled and sliced
2 small carrots, sliced
1/2 tsp. basil
1/2 tsp. marjoram

STEPS IN PREPARATION:

1. Salt and pepper beef. Brown beef in pan sprayed with non-stick spray. Add stewed tomatoes and bouillon cube. Stir in mushrooms and celery. Cover and simmer 1 hour. Add potatoes and onion, carrots and remaining seasonings. Continue cooking for another hour or until meat is tender.
2. Combine cornstarch with small amount of water, add to stew.

Serves 5

BEEF STROGANOFF

EACH SERVING Amount: 1 portion
Exchanges: 3 meat
               1/2 vegetable
               1 fat

Chol: 58 mg   Carbo: 5 gm   Fat: 14 gm
Calories: 250 Protein: 24 gm Fiber: 0
Sodium: 448 mg

INGREDIENTS:

1 1/2 lbs. lean round steak or flank steak
1/2 tsp. salt
1/4 tsp. pepper
2 Tbsp. diet margarine
1/2 lb. fresh mushrooms, sliced
1/2 C. chopped onions
1 C. beef broth
1 tsp. dried mustard
1 bay leaf
2 Tbsp. tomato paste
1 Tbsp. flour
2 Tbsp. water
3/4 C. non-fat plain yogurt

STEPS IN PREPARATION:

1. Cut meat into 1/2 inch strips, remove all fat. Pat dry steak strips with paper towel; sprinkle with salt and pepper.
2. Melt 1 Tbsp. diet margarine in non-stick frying pan, add strips of meat, cook and stir until brown on both sides. Remove meat from pan and set aside.
3. Saute onions in same pan. Saute mushrooms until almost tender. Return meat

and onions to pan.

4. Combine beef broth, mustard, bay leaf and tomato paste and pour over meat, onions, and mushroom. Cover and let simmer gently for 1/2 hour, or until meat is tender. Remove bay leaf.

5. Make smooth paste of flour and water in a cup, stir into frying pan and cook over low heat, stirring constantly until mixture thickens. Add non-fat yogurt and heat through. DO NOT BOIL. Delicious with noodles or rice. (Count those separately).

Serves 6

SPANISH RICE WITH BEEF

EACH SERVING Amount: 1 portion
Exchanges: 2 1/2 meat
              1 bread
              1 1/2 vegetable
              1/2 fat

Chol: 46 mg   **Carbo:** 34 gm **Fat:** 10 gm
Calories: 296 **Protein:** 18 gm **Fiber:** 3 gm
Sodium: 533 mg

NGREDIENTS:
1 lb. lean ground chuck
1 medium onion, chopped
1 medium green pepper, chopped
2 (16 oz.) cans stewed tomatoes, undrained
1 C. uncooked long-grain white rice
1 C. water
1 1/2 tsp. chili powder
3/4 tsp. dried oregano
1/2 tsp. salt
1/4 tsp. red pepper
1/8 tsp. garlic powder

STEPS IN PREPARATION:
1. Cook ground beef, onion, and green pepper in small dutch oven until meat is browned.
2. Drain in a colander; pat dry with a paper towel. Wipe drippings from pan with a paper towel.
3. Return meat mixture to dutch oven, and stir in remaining ingredients. Bring to a boil; cover, reduce heat, and simmer for 30 minutes or until rice is tender, stirring occasionally.

Serves 6

ORIENTAL PEPPER STEAK

EACH SERVING Amount: 1 portion
Exchanges: 3 meat
2 vegetable
1 fat

Chol: 58 mg **Carbo:** 8 gm **Fat:** 16 gm
Calories: 267 **Protein:** 23 gm **Fiber:** 2 gm
Sodium: 339 mg

INGREDIENTS:

1 Tbsp. vegetable oil
1 lb. flank or round steak, thinly sliced
1 clove garlic, minced
1 thick slice fresh ginger root
3 Tbsp. soy sauce
2 Tbsp. water
1 sm. green pepper, cut into cubes
1 sm. onion, sliced & separated into rings
2 sm. tomatoes, cut into wedges
1 C. fresh bean sprouts
2 tsp. cornstarch
1/4 C. water

STEPS IN PREPARATION:

1. Preheat oil in wok at 375 degrees. Add 1/2 of meat and stir-fry until done; push up on to side of wok. Repeat with rest of meat. Add garlic, ginger root, soy sauce and 2 Tbsp. water. Stir meat with this mixture. Cover and simmer 15 to 20 minutes. Push meat up on to side of wok.

2. Increase heat to 450. Add green pepper and onion; stir-fry 2 to 3 minutes. Push up on to

side of wok. Add tomatoes and bean sprouts; stir gently and steam 1 minute.
3. Combine cornstarch with water and stir into wok, cook until thickened.
4. Combine all ingredients.

Serves 4

OAT-STUFFED PEPPERS

EACH SERVING Amount: 1 portion
Exchanges: 1 meat
1 bread
1 vegetable

Chol: 17 mg   **Carbo:** 22 gm   **Fat:** 5 gm
Calories: 164   **Protein:** 10 gm   **Fiber:** 3 gm
Sodium: 228 mg

INGREDIENTS:
4 medium green peppers
1/2 lb. lean ground beef
1 1/2 C. quick-cooking or old-fashioned rolled
    oats (may substitute 1 1/2 C. cooked rice)
1 C. canned tomatoes, crushed
1/2 C. celery, sliced
1/4 C. onion, chopped
1/2 tsp. salt (opt.)
1/2 tsp. dried basil
1 (6 oz.) can tomato paste

STEPS IN PREPARATION:
1. Preheat oven to 350 degrees.
2. Cut peppers in half, lengthwise. Rinse and clean; set aside to drain.
3. In a large mixing bowl, combine beef, oats, tomatoes, celery, onion, salt, and basil.
4. Stuff each pepper half with 1/2 cup of beef mixture. Top each pepper half with approximately 1 Tbsp. tomato paste and spread evenly.
5. Place pepper halves in a 9 X 13 baking dish in 350 degree oven for 40 minutes.

Serves 8

STAY SLIM LASAGNA

EACH SERVING Amount: 1 portion
Exchanges: 3 meat
1 bread
11/2 vegetable
1 fat

Chol: 63 mg   **Carbo:** 32 gm   **Fat:** 16 gm
Calories: 374   **Protein:** 25 gm **Fiber:** 4 gm
Sodium: 198 mg

INGREDIENTS:
1/2 lb. ground turkey or beef
1/4 C. plus 2 Tbsp. chopped onion (reserve 2
    Tbsp. for spinach/cheese layer)
1 1/2 clove garlic, finely chopped
1/2 tsp. Italian dressing
1/2 tsp. basil
1 Tbsp. dried parsley
1/4 tsp. crushed red pepper (optional)
salt and pepper to taste
6 lasagna noodles
1 (6 oz.) can tomato paste + 1 can water
1 C. sliced fresh mushrooms or 4 oz. can
    mushrooms, drained
10 oz. fresh or frozen spinach leaves, chopped
6 oz. low-fat ricotta cheese
6 oz. mozzarella cheese shredded (reserve 3 oz.
    for top)

STEPS FOR PREPARATION:
1. Saute turkey or beef, onion, and garlic. Add
seasonings, tomato paste, and water. Simmer
about 10 minutes. Stir in mushrooms.

2. Steam fresh spinach, 2 Tbsp. onion and 1/2 clove garlic, stirring occasionally until spinach is wilted. Using wire strainer, mash out excess liquid using wire strainer. (For frozen spinach, thaw and mash out excess water.) Add 1/4 tsp. black pepper if desired. Stir until well blended. Mix in ricotta and 3 oz. mozarella.
3. Boil 6 lasagna noodles until tender; drain.
4. In 9 X 9 square or 7 X 11 casserole dish, layer 3 noodles; 1/2 meat mixture; entire spinach/cheese layer; 3 noodles; remaining meat mixture.
5. Bake at 350 degrees for 30 minutes. Top with 3 oz. mozzarella.

Serves 6

CABBAGE LASAGNA

EACH SERVING Amount: 1 portion
Exchanges: 3 meat
1/2 bread
1 vegetable
1 fat

Chol: 49 mg   **Carbo:** 23 gm **Fat:** 13 gm
Calories: 281 **Protein:** 22 gm **Fiber:** 2 gm
Sodium: 517 mg

INGREDIENTS:
1lb. lean ground beef
1 C. onion, chopped
1/2 C. green pepper, chopped
1 medium cabbage
1/2 tsp. oregano
1 tsp. salt
1/8 tsp. pepper
1 (18 oz.) can tomato paste
8 oz. mozzarella low-fat cheese, sliced

STEPS IN PREPARATION:
1. Saute ground beef, onion and pepper until meat is brown.
2. Boil cabbage until tender. Save 2 cups of the liquid from cabbage and drain off excess.
3. Combine 2 cups of the reserved cabbage liquid, oregano, salt, pepper and tomato paste. Simmer over low heat for 4 minutes. Add meat, onion and green pepper to tomato mixture. Place in a 9 X 13 pan. Layer cabbage, then remaining tomato mixture. Repeat layers. Top with slices of cheese to cover.
4. Bake at 400 degrees until cheese is browned, about 30-45 minutes.

Serves 8

APPLESAUCE MEATLOAF

EACH SERVING Amount: 1 portion
Exchanges: 3 lean meat
                    1 bread

Chol: 95 mg **Carbo:** 11 gm **Fat:** 10 gm
Calories: 272 **Protein:** 24 gm **Fiber:** 2 gm
Sodium: 733 mg

INGREDIENTS:
2 lb. ground lean meat
1 C. unsweetened applesauce
1 onion, finely diced
1 green pepper, finely diced
6 slices whole grain bread, crumbled
1 egg
2 tsp. salt
pepper to taste

STEPS IN PREPARATION:
1. Preheat oven to 350 degrees.
2. Combine all ingredients. Knead mixture with hands until well blended. Pack into loaf pan.
3. Bake for 2 hours. If desired, pour 1/2 cup tomato sauce over top of loaf before baking. For slow cooker: Pack into bottom of pot. Cover and cook on high for one hour. Then turn to low and cook for 6-8 hours. Lift out of pot, slice and serve.

Serves 8

MEXICAN MEATLOAF

EACH SERVING Amount: 1 portion
Exchanges: 2 1/2 meat
1/2 fat

Chol: 46 mg **Carbo:** 11 gm **Fat:** 10 gm
Calories: 198 **Protein:** 16 gm **Fiber:** 1 gm
Sodium: 522 mg

INGREDIENTS:

1 lb. ground turkey, thawed
1 oz. (approximately 15) tortilla chips, crushed
2 Tbsp. chopped green pepper
1 (16 oz.) can tomato sauce
1/4 C. chopped onion
1 pkg. taco seasoning mix

STEPS IN PREPARATION:

1. Reserve 1 cup of tomato sauce.
2. Combine all other ingredients. Place in 9 X 5 loaf pan.
3. Bake at 350 degrees for 45-50 minutes.
4. Heat reserved tomato sauce and serve with meatloaf.

Serves 6

FIRST PLACE CHILI

EACH SERVING Amount: 1 portion
Exchanges: 3 meat
1/2 bread
1/2 vegetable

Chol: 46 mg **Carbo:** 16 gm **Fat:** 10 gm
Calories: 221 **Protein:** 19 gm **Fiber:** 7 gm
Sodium: 866 mg

INGREDIENTS:
1 lb. extra lean ground beef
1 (8 oz.) can whole tomatoes, chopped (save liquid)
1 (15 1/2 oz.) can red kidney beans, drained
1 (12 oz.) can tomato juice
1/4 C. minced onions
1/4 tsp. pepper
1 tsp. salt
1 tsp. chili powder

STEPS IN PREPARATION:
Brown meat in skillet. Drain off fat. Stir in remaining ingredients, including liquid from tomatoes. Heat to boiling. Reduce heat and simmer 10 minutes. Serves 6

BEAN ENCHILADA BAKE

EACH SERVING Amount: 1 portion
Exchanges: 1 meat
3 bread
1/4 vegetable
1/4 milk
1/2 fat

Chol: 15 mg   **Carbo:** 55 gm **Fat:** 4 gm
Calories: 324 **Protein:** 17 gm **Fiber:** 13 gm
Sodium: 2047 mg

INGREDIENTS:
1/2 C. chopped onions
minced garlic clove
1 tsp. instant chicken bouillon
2 C. cooked pinto beans or kidney beans
2 C. tomato sauce
2 tsp. chili powder
1 tsp. cumin
salt to taste
1 C. plain non-fat yogurt
2 Tbsp. chopped green chilies
8 corn tortillas
4 oz. grated low-fat cheddar cheese

STEPS IN PREPARATION:
1. In non-stick skillet combine first 3 ingredients and cook until soft. Add beans, tomato sauce, spices. Simmer 15 minutes stirring occasionally.
2. Combine yogurt, green chilies in small bowl.

3. Line a shallow 2 1/2 qt. baking dish with 4 tortillas. Spread 1/2 yogurt mixture on tortillas. Top with 1/2 bean mixture. Repeat with remaining ingredients. Top with cheese.
4. Bake at 350 degrees for 25 minutes. Freezes well.

Serves 4

STEAK AND MUSHROOMS

EACH SERVING Amount: 1 portion
Exchanges: 2 meat
               1 fat

Chol: 34 mg   Carbo: 2 gm   Fat: 10 gm
Calories: 120   Protein: 12 gm Fiber: Tr.
Sodium: 547 mg

INGREDIENTS:

1 lb. lean beef round steak
1 1/2 tsp. salt
1 1/2 tsp. dry mustard
1 1/4 tsp. pepper
2 Tbsp. cooking oil
1 (6 oz.) can mushrooms
1 Tbsp. Worcestershire sauce

STEPS IN PREPARATION:

1. Trim fat from meat.
2. Combine salt, dry mustard, and pepper. Sprinkle over meat and pound with mallet.
3. In heavy skillet, brown steak slowly on both sides in hot oil. Drain off excess fat.
4. Drain mushrooms, reserving 1/2 cup liquid. Add mushroom liquid and Worcestershire sauce to skillet.
5. Cover tightly and cook over very low heat for 1 3/4 to 2 hours or till tender. Last few minutes, add mushrooms and heat through. Skim fat from sauce before serving.

Serves 8

CHUNKY BARBECUE BEEF

EACH SERVING Amount: 1 portion
Exchanges: 3 lean meat
                  1/2 vegetable

Chol: 59 mg   **Carbo:** 4 gm   **Fat:** 6 gm
Calories: 156 **Protein:** 21 gm **Fiber:** Tr.
Sodium: 296 mg

INGREDIENTS:
1 3/4 lbs. lean beef, cut in small cubes
1 1/2 oz. package dry onion soup mix
2 1/2 C. tomato juice
1/2 C. water
1/2 C. catsup
salt and pepper to taste

STEPS IN PREPARATION:
1. Preheat oven to 325 degrees.
2. Brown meat in large skillet sprayed with non-stick spray. Add remaining ingredients. Mix. Place in a 2 qt. casserole.
3. Cover and bake for 2 hours. More water may be added if desired. Serve over rice, noodles, or potatoes.
Serves 8

DEVILED BEEF PATTIES

EACH SERVING Amount: 1 portion
Exchanges: 3 meat
               1 bread

Chol: 122 mg Carbo: 5 gm   Fat: 10 gm
Calories: 250 Protein: 23 gm Fiber: Tr.
Sodium: 275 mg

INGREDIENTS:
1 lb. lean ground beef
1 egg
1/4 C. chili sauce
1 tsp. prepared mustard
1 tsp. prepared horseradish
1 tsp. instant minced onion
1 tsp. Worcestershire sauce
1/2 tsp. salt
dash of pepper

STEPS IN PREPARATION:
1. Combine all ingredients and shape in 4 patties.
2. Broil 3 inches from heat for 5 minutes; turn and broil 4 minutes longer or till done.
3. Serve on plain toasted 1/2 hamburger bun or 1 whole reduced calorie bun.
Serves 4

SOUTHERN HAMBURGER PIE

EACH SERVING Amount: 1 piece
Exchanges: 2 1/2 meat
1/2 bread
1/2 fat

Chol: 54 mg   **Carbo:** 14 gm   **Fat:** 9 gm
Calories: 178   **Protein:** 9 gm   **Fiber:** Tr.
Sodium: 68 mg

INGREDIENTS:

1 lb. lean ground chuck (if using ground turkey
add small amount of beef bouillon)
1 small onion, chopped
1 small can chopped green chilies
1 Tbsp. all-purpose flour
1/2 tsp. pepper
1 (5.5 oz.) can refrigerated biscuits, low-fat
1 C. low-fat cottage cheese
ground paprika
1 (4 oz.) can mushrooms, sliced and drained
4 oz. lite cream cheese, cubed
1/2 tsp. ground cumin
1/4 tsp. salt
1 egg
red pepper flakes (opt.)

STEPS IN PREPARATION:

1. Combine meat and onion in a large skillet;
   cook until meat is browned and onion is tender.
2. Drain meat mixture in colander, and pat dry
   with a paper towel; wipe pan drippings from
   skillet with a paper towel.
3. Return meat mixture to skillet; add mushrooms,
   green chilies, and lite cream cheese.

4. Cook over low heat, stirring constantly, until cheese melts. Stir in flour, salt, pepper, and cumin, blending well.
5. Split each biscuit in half; pat biscuit dough evenly into a 9" pie plate coated with non-stick spray. Spoon meat mixture over dough.
6. Combine cottage cheese and egg, mixing well; spread evenly over meat mixture. Sprinkle mixture with paprika and red pepper flakes.
7. Bake at 350 degrees for 35-40 minutes.

Serves 6

MEAT PIE

INGREDIENTS:

3 small potatoes, shredded
6 oz. grated low-fat cheddar cheese
6 eggs
3 C. skim or 1/2 % milk
1 C. green beans
1 C. sliced carrots
6 oz. turkey ham, chopped
1 C. mushroom stems and pieces
    onion, if desired

STEPS IN PREPARATION:

1. Layer potatoes and 3 oz. of cheese in the bottom of a large baking dish (at least 13 X 9).
2. Beat eggs in a bowl and mix in all the remaining ingredients. Pour over potato-cheese layer.
3. Bake 30-40 minutes at 350 degrees or until center is done. (Top with hot sauce - 1 Tbsp. is free.)

Serves 6

POULTRY

CHICKEN SUPREME

EACH SERVING Amount: 1 portion
Exchanges: 3 lean meat
1/2 bread

Chol: 61 mg **Carbo:** 13 gm **Fat:** 6 gm
Calories: 233 **Protein:** 22 gm **Fiber:** 1 gm
Sodium: 842 mg

INGREDIENTS:

6 (3 oz.) chicken breasts
1 C. bread crumbs
1 tsp. salt
1/4 tsp. black pepper
1 C. grated Parmesan cheese
2 Tbsp. parsley
1 Clove garlic, crushed
1/4 oz. slivered almonds (save a few for topping)
3 egg whites

STEPS IN PREPARATION:

1. Combine bread crumbs, Parmesan cheese, salt, pepper, parsley, garlic, and almonds.
2. Dip chicken in egg whites, and then roll in bread crumb mixture. Arrange in 9 X 13 baking dish, and sprinkle with a few slivered almonds.
3. Bake at 350 degrees for 30 minutes.

Serves 6

MUSHROOM SAUCE

EACH SERVING **Amount:** 1 portion
Exchanges: 1 fat
1/2 vegetable

Chol: Tr.　　**Carbo:** 2 gm　**Fat:** 5 gm
Calories: 55　**Protein:** 2 gm　**Fiber:** 1 gm
Sodium: 694 mg

INGREDIENTS:
1/4 C. diet margarine
2 C. sliced mushrooms
1 C. chicken broth
2 tsp. cornstarch
1 tsp. salt
pepper to taste
1 tsp. Kitchen Bouquet sauce

STEPS IN PREPARATION:
1. Saute mushrooms in melted margarine. Gradually add broth to mixture in skillet, continue to stir.
2. Dissolve cornstarch in small amount of liquid. Add to the skillet mixture, stirring constantly until thickened. Add seasonings to taste, and a small amount of Kitchen Bouquet to color. Spoon over the chicken breasts and serve. Serves 6.

CHICKEN AND PEPPERS SKILLET

EACH SERVING Amount: 1 portion
Exchanges: 3 lean meat
                 1 vegetable
                 1 fat

Chol: 49 mg **Carbo:** 6 gm **Fat:** 7 gm
Calories: 176 **Protein:** 15 gm **Fiber:** 2 gm
Sodium: 953 mg

INGREDIENTS:
2 (6 oz.) chicken breasts
3 Tbsp. soy sauce
2 tsp. cornstarch
1/8 tsp. garlic powder
sugar substitute to equal 1/8 tsp. sugar
2 med. green or red peppers
1/2 lb. mushrooms
4 Tbsp. diet margarine (divided)
1/2 C. water

STEPS IN PREPARATION:
1. Cut each chicken breast in half; remove skin and bones. Then, with knife held in slanting position, almost parallel to the cutting surface, slice across width of each half into 1/8 inch thick slices.
2. In medium bowl, mix chicken, soy sauce, cornstarch, garlic powder, and sugar substitute; set aside.
3. Cut peppers into 1/4 inch wide strips; thinly slice mushrooms.
4. In 12 inch skillet over medium heat, cook 2 table-spoons diet margarine, peppers, and mushrooms,

stirring quickly and frequently, until vegetables are tender-crisp, about 2 minutes. With slotted spoon, remove vegetables to bowl.

5. In same skillet over high heat, in 2 tablespoons diet margarine, cook chicken mixture, stirring quickly and frequently until chicken is tender, about 5 minutes. Return vegetables to skillet. Add water; heat to boiling, stirring to loosen brown bits from bottom of skillet.

Serves 4.

CHICKEN WITH SPICY FRUIT

INGREDIENTS:

1 1/4 C. unsweetened crushed pineapple
1/4 C. golden raisins
1/2 tsp. crushed red pepper
2 cloves garlic, chopped
4 (4 oz.) boned, skinned chicken breast halves
1/4 C. all fruit strawberry spread
1/4 tsp. cornstarch
green onion strips (optional)

STEPS IN PREPARATION:

1. Combine first 4 ingredients in skillet; bring to boil. Add chicken; cover, simmer for 10 minutes or until chicken is done. Remove from skillet and keep warm.
2. Bring chicken liquid to boil; cook 7 minutes or until reduced to 3/4 cup, stirring occasionally.
3. Combine strawberry spread and cornstarch; stir into cooking liquid and cook 1 minute. Serve sauce over chicken; garnish with green onion strips, if desired.

Serves 4

CURRIED CHICKEN AND RICE ✳ *good*

EACH SERVING Amount: 1 portion
Exchanges:
3 lean meat
1 bread
2 vegetable
1 fruit

Chol: 119 mg **Carbo:** 62 gm **Fat:** 5 gm
Calories: 426 **Protein:** 24 gm **Fiber:** 5 gm
Sodium: 1,239 mg

INGREDIENTS:
16 oz. skinned chicken parts
1 1/2 tsp. salt, divided
1/4 tsp. pepper
1 Tbsp. diet margarine
1/2 C. onion, minced
1/2 C. green pepper, minced
1 C. celery, diced
1 clove garlic, minced
2 tsp. curry powder
1/2 tsp. leaf thyme, crumbled
1(10 oz.) can tomatoes, coarsely chopped with
   liquid
1/2 C. raisins
1 hard-boiled egg, chopped
2 Tbsp. parsley, chopped
1 1/3 C. cooked rice

STEPS IN PREPARATION:
1. Pat chicken parts dry with paper towel and
   sprinkle with 1/2 tsp. salt and 1/4 tsp. pepper.
2. Melt margarine in large skillet and brown
   chicken pieces on both sides. Remove and
   reserve.

3. Add to skillet - onion, green pepper, celery, and garlic. Cook 5 minutes, stirring frequently. Add curry powder and thyme and cook 1 minute. Add tomatoes and liquid and 1 tsp. salt. Return chicken pieces to skillet; cover and bring to a boil. Simmer 15 minutes or until chicken is tender. (Add water if necessary.)
4. Transfer chicken to serving platter. Add raisins to sauce in skillet and cook 1 to 2 minutes. Pour sauce over chicken pieces. Sprinkle chopped hard boiled egg and chopped parsley over chicken and sauce. Serve over rice.

Serves 4

KING RANCH CHICKEN

EACH SERVING Amount: 1 portion
Exchanges: 3 meat
2 bread
1/2 vegetable
1/2 milk
1/2 fat

Chol: 50 mg   **Carbo:** 42 gm   **Fat:** 5 gm
Calories: 324   **Protein:** 22 gm   **Fiber:** 5 gm
Sodium: 1948 mg

INGREDIENTS:

8 (6 inch) corn tortillas, torn into strips
8 oz. cooked chicken, diced
2 Tbsp. flour
1 tsp. salt
2 chicken broth cubes
2 Tbsp. tomato paste
2 C. skim milk (minus 2 Tbs.)
1 C. water
1/2 C. canned mushrooms, drained, sliced
2 (4 oz.) cans chopped green chilies
1/4 C. chopped onions
4 oz. grated low-fat cheddar cheese

STEPS IN PREPARATION:

1. Layer 1/2 of tortilla strips and chicken in a casserole dish sprayed with non-stick spray. Repeat layer.
2. In saucepan, combine flour, salt, chicken cubes and tomato paste. Gradually add milk until thickened. Remove from heat. Stir in water, mushrooms, chilies, and onion.

3. Pour sauce over chicken and tortilla strips. Sprinkle evenly with cheese. Cover with foil and refrigerate overnight.
4. Bake covered at 300 degrees for approx. 1 hr. 15 min.

Serves 4.

COUNTRY CAPTAIN

EACH SERVING **Amount:** 1 portion
Exchanges: 4 lean meat
1 bread
2 vegetable

Chol: 66 mg **Carbo:** 47 gm **Fat:** 3 gm
Calories: 347 **Protein:** 24 gm **Fiber:** 3 gm
Sodium: 1160 mg

INGREDIENTS:
1 lb. boned skinned chicken thighs or breasts
1/2 tsp. each garlic salt and paprika
1 C. onion, chopped
2 medium green peppers, seeded and chopped
3/4 tsp. garlic powder
2 C. canned tomatoes, undrained
1/2 C. tomato paste
1 Tbsp. dehydrated parsley flakes
sugar substitute to equal 2 tsp. sugar
1/2 tsp. thyme
1/2 tsp. curry powder
1 tsp. sherry extract
1/4 tsp. black pepper
3 chicken bouillon cubes, dissolved in 1/4 C.
     boiling water
1 1/3 C. cooked rice

STEPS IN PREPARATION:
1. Sprinkle chicken with garlic salt and paprika.
   Brown in a large non-stick skillet over medium
   heat. Remove chicken and set aside.
2. Add onion, peppers and garlic powder to the
   skillet. Cook about 4 minutes or until vegetables
   begin to wilt. Add next 8 ingredients and stir

until well combined. Add bouillon and reserved chicken; cook, covered, about 40 minutes or until chicken is tender. Divide evenly and serve each portion over 1/3 cup hot rice.
Serves 4.

TEXAS GOLDEN CHICKEN

EACH SERVING Amount: 1 portion
Exchanges: 3 lean meat
1/2 bread

Chol: 87 mg **Carbo:** 8 gm **Fat:** 5 gm
Calories: 171 **Protein:** 23 gm **Fiber:** Tr.
Sodium: 450 mg

INGREDIENTS:
8 chicken legs, skinned
2 Tbsp. orange juice concentrate
6 Tbsp. seasoned bread crumbs
1/2 tsp. salt
1/8 tsp. black pepper
1/2 tsp. paprika
1/8 tsp. cayenne pepper

STEPS IN PREPARATION:
1. Puncture drumsticks with a fork and brush with orange juice concentrate.
2. Spray a non-stick jelly-roll pan with cooking spray.
3. Combine bread crumbs, salt, black pepper, paprika, and cayenne pepper in a plastic bag; add chicken and shake well to coat lightly. Arrange chicken in a single layer in pan.
4. Bake, without turning, at 450 degrees for 30 minutes or until crisp and golden brown. Blot with paper towel for extra crispness. Best served at once.

Serves 4

TENDER BAKED CHICKEN

EACH SERVING Amount: 2 ounces
Exchanges: 2 meat

Chol: 40 mg   **Carbo:** 3 gm   **Fat:** 3 gm
Calories: 105 **Protein:** 17 gm **Fiber:** Tr.
Sodium: 270 mg

INGREDIENTS:
1 chicken, cut into frying pieces, skinned
1 C. prepared non-fat chicken bouillon
1 Tbsp. Worcestershire sauce
1 Tbsp. rosemary
2 Tbsp. minced onion
2 Tbsp. chopped bell pepper
seasonings; such as salt, celery salt, or
    seasoning salt

STEPS IN PREPARATION:
1. Place chicken pieces in 13 X 9 baking dish.
2. Stir Worcestershire sauce into bouillon.
3. Sprinkle remaining ingredients on chicken.
4. Pour sauce over chicken. Cover with aluminum foil.
5. Bake for 45-60 minutes at 400 degrees.

CHICKEN-VEGETABLE TETRAZZINI

EACH SERVING Amount: 1 portion
Exchanges: 3 meat
2 bread
1/4 vegetable
3/4 fat

Chol: 67 mg **Carbo:** 36 gm **Fat:** 4 gm
Calories: 324 **Protein:** 26 gm **Fiber:** 6 gm
Sodium: 289 mg

INGREDIENTS:

16 oz. boned, skinned chicken breast, cut
into strips
2 cloves garlic, minced
1 C. frozen green peas
1 C. fresh mushrooms, quartered
1 Tbsp. diet margarine
2 Tbsp. flour
3/4 C. + 2 Tbsp. skim milk
2 Tbsp. diced pimiento
1/4 tsp. salt
1/4 tsp. pepper
2 C. hot cooked spaghetti

STEPS IN PREPARATION:

1. Place chicken and garlic in a 2 qt. glass measure. Cover with heavy-duty plastic wrap and vent.
2. Microwave at medium-high (70%) 4 minutes, stirring once. Add peas; cover and microwave at medium-high 4 minutes stirring once. Stir in mushrooms; cover and microwave at medium-high 2-3 minutes or until chicken is done. Drain well and set aside.

3. Place margarine in 2 C. glass measure; micro-wave to melt. Add flour; stir well. Gradually add milk, stirring well; microwave at high 4 minutes or until thickened. Stir in pimiento and next 3 ingredients; set aside.
4. Combine chicken mixture & pasta in large bowl. Toss well.

Serves 4.

CHICKEN CORDON BLEU

EACH SERVING **Amount:** 1 portion
Exchanges: 3 meat
1/2 bread
1/2 fat

Chol: 65 mg **Carbo:** 6 gm **Fat:** 8 gm
Calories: 200 **Protein:** 18 gm **Fiber:** Tr.
Sodium: 173 mg

INGREDIENTS:

6 (3 oz.) chicken breasts, boned and skinned
6 thin slices of fat-free ham, 1/3 oz. each
6 slices low-fat Swiss cheese, 1/2 oz. each
1/4 C. flour
2 Tbsp. diet margarine
1 tsp. chicken-flavored gravy base
1 (4-oz.) can sliced mushrooms, drained
2 Tbsp. flour
toasted sliced almonds

STEPS IN PREPARATION:

1. Roll chicken pieces, boned side up, on cutting board. Working from center out, pound chicken with a wooden mallet to make cutlets 1/4 inch thick. Sprinkle with salt.

2. Place a ham slice and cheese slice on each cutlet. Tuck in sides of each and roll up as for a jelly roll. Skewer or tie securely.

3. Coat rolls with 1/4 cup flour. In a skillet brown in margarine, and remove to 11 X 7 X 1-1/2 inch baking pan.

4. In the same skillet, combine 1/2 cup water, the gravy base, and mushrooms. Heat, stirring in the

CHICKEN–BROCCOLI CASSEROLE

EACH SERVING Amount: 1 portion
Exchanges: 2 1/2 meat
1/2 bread
1 vegetable
1/3 milk
1 fat

Chol: 54 mg   **Carbo:** 13 gm **Fat:** 9 gm
Calories: 216 **Protein:** 18 gm **Fiber:** 1 gm
Sodium: 857 mg

INGREDIENTS:

3 C. cooked broccoli cuts
12 oz. chicken (cooked, cut into chunks)
1/2 tsp. lemon juice
6 Tbsp. lite mayonnaise
2 chicken bouillon cubes
2 C. skim milk (or 1/2 %)
2 1/2 Tbsp. flour
1/2 tsp. curry powder
6 oz. grated low-fat cheddar cheese
2 slices bread (crumbled)
1 Tbsp. diet margarine

STEPS IN PREPARATION:

1. Layer broccoli in a 13 X 9" baking dish.
2. Layer chicken on top of broccoli.
3. Mix lemon juice, mayonnaise, bouillon cubes, skim milk, flour and curry powder in a saucepan. Cook over medium-high heat until sauce thickens.
4. Pour this sauce over the broccoli and chicken. Next, add a layer of cheese.

5. Melt the butter and pour it over the bread crumbs. Put this mixture on top as the last layer.
6. Bake at 350 degrees for 30 minutes.

Serves 6

CHICKEN VEGETABLE PIE

EACH SERVING **Amount:** 1 portion
Exchanges: 2 meat
1/2 bread
1 vegetable
1/2 fat

Chol: 134 mg **Carbo:** 19 gm **Fat:** 6 gm
Calories: 198 **Protein:** 16 gm **Fiber:** 6 gm
Sodium: 904 mg

INGREDIENTS:
1 pkg. frozen cauliflower
1 (6 oz.) can cooked chicken
1 pkg. frozen broccoli
4 oz. grated low-fat cheese
1 sm. can mushroom pieces
11/2 C. skim milk
3/4 C. Buttermilk Baking mix
3 eggs
1 tsp. salt
1/4 tsp. pepper

STEPS IN PREPARATION:
1. Spray 10" pie plate with non-stick spray.
2. In pie plate mix uncooked, defrosted cauliflower and broccoli, chicken with cheese, and mushrooms.
3. Beat all other ingredients until smooth and pour over mixture in pie plate.
4. Bake 45-60 minutes at 350 degrees.
Serves 6.

TURKEY POT PIE

EACH SERVING Amount: 1 portion
Exchanges: 2 meat
1 1/2 vegetable
1 bread
1 fat

Chol: 2 mg **Carbo:** 34 gm **Fat:** 12 gm
Calories: 252 **Protein:** 6 gm **Fiber:** 2 gm
Sodium: 1005 mg

INGREDIENTS:

8 oz. diced turkey
1 Tbsp. flour
1 C. chopped onion
1/4 C. celery, chopped
1/2 tsp. thyme
1/8 tsp. pepper
1 tsp. diet margarine
1 C. sliced carrots
1/2 C. water
1 (10 1/4 oz.) can mushroom soup
1 C. cooked green beans
1 (5 ct.) can biscuits (be sure the fat grams are
  less than 2)

STEPS IN PREPARATION:

1. Preheat oven 350 degrees.
2. Toss turkey with flour.
3. Cook onion, celery, thyme, pepper in margarine. Add carrots, water, soup, beans, turkey.
   Pour into 2 quart casserole. Split biscuits, put
   on top.
4. Bake 30 minutes.

Serves 4.

FISH

SHRIMP CREOLE

EACH SERVING Amount: 1 cup
Exchanges: 2 meat
                   1 vegetable
                   1 bread

Chol: 173 mg **Carbo:** 33 gm **Fat:** 3 gm
Calories: 237 **Protein:** 30 gm **Fiber:** 4 gm
Sodium: 1559 mg

INGREDIENTS:

20 shrimp (8 oz.)
2 C. (16 oz. can) tomato sauce
1 small onion, chopped
1 celery stalk, chopped
1/4 green bell pepper, diced
1/4 C. sliced mushrooms
3 Tbsp. parsley
1/2 tsp. pepper
1 to 1 1/2 C. brown rice, prepared according to package directions (not included in exchanges)

STEPS IN PREPARATION:

1. Peel, de-vein, and wash shrimp; set aside. (If shrimp are frozen, let them thaw first in refrigerator.)
2. Simmer tomato sauce, onion, celery, green pepper, mushrooms, parsley and pepper in skillet for 30 minutes. Add shrimp and cook 10-15 minutes more, until shrimp are tender. Serve over brown rice.

Serves 2

CRAB STUFFED SOLE

Chol: 65 mg **Carbo:** 5 gm **Fat:** 2 gm
Calories: 119 **Protein:** 21 gm **Fiber:** 1 gm
Sodium: 406 mg

INGREDIENTS:

1/4 C. chopped onion
1 tsp. diet margarine
1 (6 oz.) can crab meat, rinsed and drained
1/2 tsp. parsley flakes
1/2 tsp. lemon pepper
1/2 C. tomato juice
1/2 tsp. basil
3 slices lemon, halved
1/4 C. chopped green pepper
2 Tbsp. bread crumbs
1/2 tsp. salt
2 sole filets (8 oz. each)
1/4 tsp. oregano
1/4 C. lemon juice

STEPS IN PREPARATION:

1. Combine onion and green pepper with 1 tsp. diet margarine. In non-stick pan, cook on low heat until tender. Stir in crab meat, bread crumbs, parsley, salt, and lemon pepper to make stuffing. Set aside.
2. Arrange half of sole on roasting rack. Spoon on stuffing mixture; cover with second filet. Set aside.
3. Mix tomato juice, oregano, basil and lemon juice to make sauce. Heat until bubbly.

Pour 1/4 cup sauce over filets. Top with lemon slices.
4. Cover and cook at 350 degrees until center is hot and fish is flaky. Serve with the rest of the sauce.

Serves 6.

HEALTHY HALIBUT OR FLOUNDER

EACH SERVING Amount: 1 portion
Exchanges: 2-1/2 meat
                 1 vegetable

Chol: 36 mg   **Carbo:** 8 gm   **Fat:** 3 gm
Calories: 167 **Protein:** 25 gm **Fiber:** 3 gm
Sodium: 74 mg

INGREDIENTS:
1/2 C. fresh mushrooms
2/3 C. onions
1/3 C. tomatoes
1/4 C. green pepper
1 Tbsp. parsley
3 Tbsp. pimiento
1 lb. fish
salt & pepper to taste
1 pkg. dry butter flavoring (We used Butter Buds.
    Follow instructions on package for making into
    liquid.)
2 Tbsp. lemon juice

STEPS IN PREPARATION:
1. Place vegetables in microwave dish, cover
   with plastic and microwave on high 3-4
   minutes. Add parsley and pimiento. Set aside.
2. Arrange fish in skillet, salt and pepper then
   brown on each side.
3. Drain vegetables and discard liquid. Pour
   vegetables on top of fish. Pour butter flavoring
   and lemon over all.
4. Cover dish and cook until fish flakes apart with
   fork.
Serves 4.

OVEN-FRIED CATFISH

EACH SERVING Amount: 1 portion
Exchanges: 3 lean meat
1/2 bread
1/2 fat

Chol: 77 mg Carbo: 5 gm Fat: 14 gm
Calories: 275 Protein: 26 gm Fiber: 1 gm
Sodium: 658 mg

INGREDIENTS:

11/4 lbs. whole, headless catfish (4)
2 Tbsp. non-fat plain yogurt
2 tsp. vegetable oil
11/2 tsp. lemon juice
1/4 tsp. paprika
1/2 tsp. salt
1/8 tsp. pepper
4 Tbsp. dry whole wheat bread crumbs

STEPS IN PREPARATION:

1. Wash and drain fish.
2. Combine yogurt, oil, lemon juice, and seasonings in shallow dish.
3. Sprinkle bread crumbs on waxed paper. Dip fish in yogurt mixture, then press in crumbs, lightly coating both sides. Place fish on lightly greased cookie sheet or shallow baking pan.
4. Bake in 475 degree oven for 10 minutes or until done.

Serves 4

TASTY COD

EACH SERVING Amount: 1 portion
Exchanges: 2-1/2 lean meat
1 vegetable

Chol: 3 mg **Carbo:** 27 gm **Fat:** 5 gm
Calories: 158 **Protein:** 25 gm **Fiber:** 1 gm
Sodium: 77 mg

INGREDIENTS:

1 1/2 lbs. frozen cod fillet
1/4 tsp. salt
1/4 tsp. pepper
1 tsp. tarragon
1 Tbsp. lemon juice
1 C. chopped mushrooms
1 C. thinly sliced carrots
1/2 C. chopped celery
2 Tbsp. fresh chopped parsley
Diet margarine

STEPS IN PREPARATION:

1. Place the frozen fish on a sheet of aluminum foil; lightly salt and pepper. Sprinkle with tarragon and lemon juice. Add all the chopped vegetables and the fresh parsley. Dot with diet margarine and wrap well.
2. Bake at 350 degrees for 35-40 minutes.

Serves 6

SALMON-NOODLE BAKE

EACH SERVING Amount: 1 cup
Exchanges: 2 lean meat
2 bread

Chol: 22 mg   **Carbo:** 28 gm **Fat:** 8 gm
Calories: 252 **Protein:** 16 gm **Fiber:** 1 gm
Sodium: 359 mg

INGREDIENTS:
2 oz. noodles
3 C. water
2 tsp. diet margarine
1 Tbsp. flour
2/3 C. skim milk
1 Tbsp. chopped onion
1/16 tsp. pepper
1 (4 oz.) can salmon
2 tsp. lite mayonnaise

STEPS IN PREPARATION:
1. Cook noodles according to package directions and drain.
2. In small saucepan, melt margarine, stir in flour, and cook 1 minute. Add milk, stir until blended, bring to a boil, and cook 2 minutes, stirring constantly. Add onion and pepper to sauce.
3. Drain salmon and reserve juice. Remove bones and flake salmon. Add 6 Tbsp. juice, mayonnaise, and sauce. Stir. Add noodles and mix.
4. Put in 2-quart casserole dish that has been sprayed with vegetable cooking spray. Bake in 350° oven for 30 minutes.

Serves 2

SALMON OAT PATTIES

EACH SERVING Amount: 2 patties
Exchanges: 2 meat
                1/2 bread

Chol: 38 mg   Carbo: 13 gm Fat: 7 gm
Calories: 165 Protein: 23 gm Fiber: 1 gm
Sodium: 501 mg

INGREDIENTS:

1 (15 1/2 oz.) can pink salmon
1 small sweet onion, chopped
2 egg whites
1/2 C. quick cooking oatmeal
non-stick spray

STEPS IN PREPARATION:

1. Preheat oven to 375 degrees.
2. Drain salmon and remove any large bones or skin.
3. In medium mixing bowl, flake salmon and add chopped onion, egg whites, and oatmeal. Mix well; divide and form into 8 patties.
4. Spray non-stick spray on baking sheet. Place patties on sheet.
5. Bake at 375 degrees for 10 to 12 minutes on each side.

Serves 4.

TUNA CAKES

EACH SERVING Amount: 2 patties
Exchanges: 3 lean meat
                   2 vegetable
                   2 bread

Chol: 106 mg **Carbo:** 9 gm   **Fat:** 5 gm
Calories: 169 **Protein:** 11 gm **Fiber:** 3 gm
Sodium: 600 mg

INGREDIENTS:

1 C. shredded zucchini (about 4 ounces)
2 Tbsp. chopped onion
1/2 tsp. minced garlic clove
2 tsp. diet margarine (divided)
1 (6 1/2 oz.) can tuna packed in water
1 egg
1 (1/2 C.) whole wheat bread cubes (about 3
    slices)
1/4 tsp. salt
1/4 tsp. pepper

STEPS IN PREPARATION:

1. Saute zucchini, onion, and garlic in 1 tsp. margarine about 5 minutes. Mix with remaining ingredients until blended.
2. Form into 6 patties and brown in margarine in large skillet over medium heat, about 3 minutes per side. Serve with lemon or horseradish dip.

Serves 3

CHEESE-TUNA-RICE MUFFINLETTES

EACH SERVING Amount: 1 portion
Exchanges: 3 meat
1 bread
1 fat

Chol: 160 mg **Carbo:** 31 gm **Fat:** 14 gm
Calories: 283 **Protein:** 25 gm **Fiber:** 1 gm
Sodium: 667 mg

INGREDIENTS:
2 C. cooked rice
8 oz. shredded low-fat cheddar cheese
2 C. tuna, drained and flaked
3/4 C. chopped celery
1 Tbsp. instant chopped onion
1 Tbsp. parsley flakes
1 tsp. season salt
2 eggs, beaten
2 Tbsp. skim milk
non-stick spray

Tangy Butter Sauce
3 Tbsp. melted diet margarine
1 Tbsp. lemon juice
1/2 tsp. season salt
1/2 tsp. parsley flakes

STEPS IN PREPARATION:
1. Combine rice, cheese, tuna, celery, onion, parsley, and season salt. Stir in eggs and milk, mixing thoroughly.
2. Spray six muffin cups with non-stick spray. Divide rice mixture evenly among cups.

3. Bake at 375 degrees for 15 minutes or until lightly browned. Loosen with spatula.
4. Combine ingredients for Tangy Butter Sauce and spoon over muffinlettes.

Serves 4

BAKED TUNA LOAF WITH CUCUMBER SAUCE

EACH SERVING Amount: 1 portion
Exchanges: 1 1/2 lean meat
1/2 bread

Chol: 53 mg **Carbo:** 11 gm **Fat:** 3 gm
Calories: 133 **Protein:** 17 gm **Fiber:** 1 gm
Sodium: 227 mg

INGREDIENTS:
Loaf
2 (6 1/2 oz.) cans tuna packed in water, drained
3/4 C. finely chopped celery
3/4 C. oats (quick or old fashioned, uncooked)
1/2 C. skim milk
1 egg
1/8 tsp. pepper

Cucumber Sauce
8 oz. plain non-fat yogurt
1/2 medium cucumber, finely chopped
2 Tbsp. chopped fresh dill or 1 tsp. dried dill weed
1 tsp. minced onion.

STEPS IN PREPARATION:
1. Heat oven to 350 degrees.
2. Coat 8 x 4 inch loaf pan with non-stick spray.
3. Flake tuna; add remaining ingredients, mixing well. Pat into prepared pan.
4. Bake 40 minutes; let stand for 5 minutes before slicing. Serve warm or cold with Cucumber Sauce.
5. In small bowl, combine yogurt, cucumber, dill and minced onion; mix well. Chill.
Serves 8

SALADS

SIMPLE SALAD

EACH SERVING Amount: 1 cup
Exchanges: 1 vegetable

Chol: 0   **Carbo:** 6 gm   **Fat:** 0
Calories: 33   **Protein:** 3 gm   **Fiber:** 2 gm
Sodium: 38 mg

INGREDIENTS:

1 bag frozen broccoli/cauliflower cuts (20 oz.)
1 (8 oz.) carton plain non-fat yogurt
1 Tbsp. dill weed
1 tsp. celery salt

STEPS IN PREPARATION:

1. Cook broccoli/cauliflower according to package directions.
2. Cool.
3. Combine yogurt with spices.
4. Blend vegetables with yogurt and chill overnight.

Serves 4

EASY SPINACH SALAD

EACH SERVING **Amount:** 1 portion
Exchanges: 1 meat
2 vegetable
1/4 fruit
1/2 fat

Chol: 213 mg **Carbo:** 28 gm **Fat:** 6 gm
Calories: 217 **Protein:** 19 gm **Fiber:** 14 gm
Sodium: 321 mg

INGREDIENTS:
4 C. fresh spinach, washed, torn, and then chilled
1/2 C. red onion - sliced
1/2 C. mushrooms - sliced
2 hard boiled eggs - chopped
1 small can unsweetened mandarin oranges -
chilled and drained
3 green onions - chopped (if desired)
2 tsp. imitation bacon
2 servings oil-free dressing

STEPS IN PREPARATION:
Toss together.
Serves 2

CARROT AND RAISIN SALAD

EACH SERVING Amount: 1 portion
Exchanges: 1/2 vegetable
1/2 fruit
1/2 fat

Chol: 3 mg   **Carbo:** 14 gm **Fat:** 3 gm
Calories: 85   **Protein:** 1 gm **Fiber:** 1 gm
Sodium: 159 mg

INGREDIENTS:

6 Tbsp. raisins, washed and drained

2 C. grated carrots

1 C. drained, crushed pineapple

1/3 C. lite mayonnaise

1 Tbsp. lemon juice

1/4 tsp. salt

2 pkgs. sugar substitute

STEPS IN PREPARATION:

1. Toss raisins, carrots and pineapple together.
2. Set aside.
3. Stir together mayonnaise, lemon juice, salt, and sweetener. Add to carrot mixture.
4. Keep refrigerated.

Serves 8

FRUIT SALAD

Chol: 0   Carbo: 20 gm   Fat: 0
Calories: 77   Protein: 1 gm   Fiber: 2 gm
Sodium: 2 mg

INGREDIENTS:

3/4 C. pineapple chunks, drained, reserving juice
1/2 C. pineapple juice
1 Tbsp. cornstarch
1- 3 oz. banana
1 kiwi fruit
1 C. strawberries
1 small apple
(or substitute your favorite fruits)

STEPS IN PREPARATION:

1. Thicken pineapple juice with 1 Tbsp. cornstarch in a saucepan over medium heat. (It helps to mix the cornstarch with a little bit of water before adding the juice so it won't be lumpy.) You may add 1 package sugar substitute to the sauce when cooled, if desired.
2. Pour over fruit and stir.

Serves 6

CRANBERRY RELISH

EACH SERVING Amount: 1/2 cup
Exchanges: 1 fruit

Chol: 0   Carbo: 18 gm   Fat: 0
Calories: 71   Protein: 0   Fiber: 4 gm
Sodium: 1 mg

INGREDIENTS:
1 thin-skinned orange, seeded and chopped
1 1/3 C. fresh cranberries
1 medium apple, unpeeled and chopped
1 (8 oz.) can unsweetened pineapple tidbits,
   drained

STEPS IN PREPARATION:
1. Position knife blade in food processor bowl;
   add orange.
2. Cover with top; process 3 minutes or until
   orange peel is finely chopped.
3. Add remaining ingredients, and pulse 4 times,
   scraping sides of processor bowl between
   each pulse.
4. Cover and chill.
Yields 2 1/2 cups.

EASY COLESLAW

EACH SERVING Amount: 1 portion
Exchanges: 1 vegetable
                   1/2 fat

Chol: 3 mg   **Carbo:** 5 gm   **Fat:** 3 gm
Calories: 44   **Protein:** 1 gm   **Fiber:** 1 gm
Sodium: 218 mg

INGREDIENTS:
5 C. shredded cabbage
1/4 C. shredded carrots
1/4 C. chopped green pepper
2 Tbsp. minced onion
1/4 C. chopped celery

Combine in a large bowl. Mix well and set aside.

Dressing: 4 Tbsp. lite mayonnaise
          1 Tbsp. vinegar
          1/2 tsp. salt
          1/2 tsp. celery seed
          1/4 C. skim milk

STEPS IN PREPARATION:
1. Mix dressing ingredients together, pour over vegetables and toss well.
2. Refrigerate until ready to serve.
Serves 8

TEXAS MUSTARD SLAW

EACH SERVING Amount: 1 portion
Exchanges: 1 vegetable
1 fat

Chol: 6 mg   **Carbo:** 8 gm   **Fat:** 7 gm
Calories: 98   **Protein:** 1 gm   **Fiber:** 1 gm
Sodium: 563 mg

INGREDIENTS:
1 large cabbage
1 C. chopped dill pickles
3/4 C. chopped onions
1 C. lite mayonnaise
2 Tbsp. prepared mustard
1 pkg. sugar substitute
1 tsp. celery seeds
2 tsp. vinegar
1/8 tsp. pepper

STEPS IN PREPARATION:
1. Shred enough cabbage to make 12 cups.
2. Combine cabbage, pickles, and onions in large bowl; set aside.
3. Combine mayonnaise and remaining ingredients in a bowl; stir well.
4. Pour over cabbage mixture; toss. Cover and chill.
Serves 12

MOCK POTATO SALAD

EACH SERVING **Amount:** 1/2 cup
Exchanges: 1/4 meat
1 vegetable
1/2 fat

Chol: 56 mg   **Carbo:** 4 gm   **Fat:** 4 gm
Calories: 61   **Protein:** 3 gm   **Fiber:** 1 gm
Sodium: 262 mg

INGREDIENTS:
1 large bag frozen cauliflower
4 Tbsp. lite mayonnaise
1 large dill pickle, chopped
1 small onion, chopped
2 hard boiled eggs, chopped

STEPS IN PREPARATION:
1. Prepare 1 large bag of frozen cauliflower according to directions and let cool.
2. Cut into small pieces.
3. Combine remaining ingredients thoroughly and chill before serving.
Serves 8

FANCY TUNA SALAD

EACH SERVING Amount: 1 portion
Exchanges: 2 meats
1 bread
2 vegetables
1/2 fruit
1 fat

Chol: 53 mg   **Carbo:** 33 gm **Fat:** 7 gm
Calories: 312 **Protein:** 28 gm **Fiber:** 7 gm
Sodium: 488 mg

INGREDIENTS:

1/2 C. water-packed tuna, drained
1/2 C. tiny green peas, drained
1 C. assorted chopped salad vegetables:
   onions, celery, and grated carrots
1/2 small apple, pared and grated
1 Tbsp. lite mayonnaise

STEPS IN PREPARATION:

Mix all together.
Serves 1

TUNA SALAD

EACH SERVING Amount: 1 portion
Exchanges: 2 meats
3/4 fat

Chol: 157 mg   **Carbo:** 1 gm   **Fat:** 7 gm
Calories: 180   **Protein:** 26 gm **Fiber:** 0
Sodium: 454

INGREDIENTS
1 (6 1/8 oz.) can tuna in water
1 Tbsp. lite mayonnaise
1 1/2 Tbsp. dill pickle relish
1 tsp. mustard
1 hard boiled egg, chopped

STEPS IN PREPARATION
Mix all ingredients together.
Serves 2.

ASPARAGUS-PASTA SALAD

EACH SERVING Amount: 1 portion
Exchanges: 2 meats
1 bread
1/2 vegetable
1 fat

Chol: 24 mg **Carbo:** 25 gm **Fat:** 11 gm
Calories: 250 **Protein:** 13 gm **Fiber:** 2 gm
Sodium: 624 mg

INGREDIENTS:

4 oz. uncooked spiral pasta
6 fresh asparagus stalks or 3/4 C. thawed frozen
cut asparagus (may substitute green beans)
1/4 C. coarsely chopped red onion
7 oz. cooked lean ham, diced
1 oz. crumbled low-fat blue cheese
4 red leaf lettuce leaves
4 lemon slices

LEMON-TARRAGON DRESSING:

1 Tbsp. vegetable oil
1 Tbsp. plus 1 tsp. tarragon-flavored vinegar or
wine vinegar
1 Tbsp. plus 2 tsp. water
1/4 tsp. grated lemon peel
1/8 tsp. dried leaf tarragon, crushed
1 tsp. beaten egg

STEPS IN PREPARATION:

1. Prepare Lemon-Tarragon Dressing; refrigerate until served.
To make Lemon-Tarragon Dressing: In a small bowl, combine all dressing ingredients. Beat with a whisk until blended. Combine with salad. Makes 1/4 cup dressing.

2. Cook pasta in lightly salted water, 5-7 minutes. Drain; rinse with cold water. Pour into a large bowl; cover.
3. Cut fresh asparagus in 1" pieces. Steam fresh asparagus about 3 minutes. Cool quickly in cold water.
4. Drain cooked fresh asparagus or thawed frozen asparagus on paper towels.
5. Add asparagus pieces, onion, ham and cheese to pasta; toss gently to distribute.
6. Pour dressing over pasta mixture; toss again.
7. Cover and refrigerate until ready to serve, up to 3 days.
8. Arrange 1 lettuce leaf on each of 4 plates. Spoon salad equally onto lettuce-lined plates.
9. Cut each lemon slice from center through peel. Twist cut edges of peel in opposite directions, making lemon twist. Garnish each salad.

Serves 4

HOT CHICKEN SALAD

EACH SERVING Amount: 1 portion
Exchanges: 2 meat
1/2 vegetable
1 fat

Chol: 53 mg   **Carbo:** 4 gm   **Fat:** 11 gm
Calories: 190 **Protein:** 17 gm **Fiber:** Tr.
Sodium: 566 mg

INGREDIENTS:
2 C. diced chicken
1 1/2 C. diced celery
1/2 oz. slivered toasted almonds
1 Tbsp. grated onion
1 Tbsp. lemon juice
1/2 tsp. salt, pepper, tabasco
1/2 C. diet mayonnaise
2 oz. grated low-fat cheddar cheese

STEPS IN PREPARATION:
1. Toss together all ingredients except cheese in baking dish.
2. Top with cheese and bake at 375 degrees until cheese bubbles.

Serves 6.

CHERRY WALDORF SALAD

EACH SERVING Amount: 1 portion
Exchanges: 1/2 fruit

Chol: 0   **Carbo:** 12 gm   **Fat:** Tr.
Calories: 43   **Protein:** 1 gm   **Fiber:** 2 gm
Sodium: 57 mg

INGREDIENTS:

1 small pkg. cherry flavor sugar-free gelatin
dash of salt
3/4 C. boiling water
1/2 C. cold water
Ice cubes
1/2 C. diced peeled apple
1 medium banana, sliced or diced
1/4 C. sliced celery

STEPS IN PREPARATION:

1. Dissolve gelatin and salt in boiling water.
2. Combine cold water and ice cubes to make 1 1/4 cups. Add to gelatin and stir until slightly thickened; remove any unmelted ice.
3. Fold in fruits and celery. Chill in bowl until set, about 2 hours.

Serves 4

STRAWBERRY CRUNCH

EACH SERVING Amount: 1 portion
Exchanges: 1 fruit
1/2 fat

Chol: 0   **Carbo:** 15 gm   **Fat:** 2 gm
Calories: 84   **Protein:** 2 gm   **Fiber:** 2 gm
Sodium: 41 mg

INGREDIENTS:
2 small pkg. strawberry sugar-free gelatin
1 C. boiling water
4 C. unsweetened frozen strawberries
1C. crushed pineapple drained (unsweetened)
3 mashed bananas
1/3 C. pecans
1/2 C. non-fat plain yogurt

STEPS IN PREPARATION:
1. Mix gelatin and water until dissolved.
2. Add fruit and blend and then add nuts.
3. Pour 1/2 of mixture into a 9 X 13 pan and chill
   for 1 hour. Reserve remaining mixture at room
   temperature. After bottom of mixture is set,
   spread with yogurt. Top with remaining gelatin.
4. Chill until firm.
Serves 12

STRAWBERRY SALAD

EACH SERVING Amount: 1 portion
Exchanges: 1/2 fruit
               1/2 fat

Chol: 3 mg   **Carbo:** 8 gm   **Fat:** 2 gm
Calories: 49   **Protein:** 1 gm   **Fiber:** 1 gm
Sodium: 30 mg

INGREDIENTS:

1 large box strawberry gelatin (sugar-free)
1 (20 oz.) pkg. frozen strawberries (unsweetened)
1 (8 oz.) can pineapple, crushed (unsweetened)
3 packages sugar substitute
2 bananas, mashed
1 C. sour cream (low-fat) see page 194

STEPS IN PREPARATION:

1. Thaw the strawberries and mash them.
2. Dissolve gelatin in 2 cups of boiling water.
3. Add strawberries which have been sweetened with 3 pkg. sugar substitute. Add the pineapple and bananas.
4. Divide the recipe in half. Put in a dish or gelatin mold and put in the refrigerator.
5. When this half has set, spread on the sour cream and pour on the remaining half. Return to the refrigerator.

Serves 16

LIME-PINEAPPLE GELATIN SALAD

EACH SERVING Amount: 1 portion
Exchanges: 1 fruit
              1/8 milk

Chol: 0   Carbo: 15 gm Fat: Tr.
Calories: 72 Protein: 3 gm Fiber: Tr.
Sodium: 71 mg

INGREDIENTS:
1 pkg. lime sugar-free gelatin
1 1/3 C. crushed pineapple (in own juice, drained)
1/2 C. non-fat yogurt

STEPS IN PREPARATION:
1. Prepare gelatin as directed on package; chill until almost but not completely set.
2. Add yogurt to gelatin and whip with electric mixer until well blended.
3. Fold in pineapple, pour into 4 containers and chill until set.

Serves 4

Variation: Carrot-Pineapple Gelatin
    1 pkg. orange gelatin
    1 1/3 c. crushed pineapple
    1 c. grated raw carrots
    Omit yogurt and 1/8 milk exchange

ORANGE CHIFFON

EACH SERVING Amount: 1 portion
Exchanges: 1/2 fruit
2/3 fat

Chol: 0 **Carbo:** 9 gm **Fat:** 1 gm
Calories: 54 **Protein:** 1 gm **Fiber:** 1 gm
Sodium: 50 mg

INGREDIENTS:

3 oranges, sectioned
3/4 C. boiling water
1 small pkg. orange flavor sugar-free gelatin
1/2 C. cold water
Ice cubes
1 C. sugar-free whipped topping
1 tsp. grated orange rind (optional)

STEPS IN PREPARATION:

1. Spoon orange sections into 6 dessert glasses.
2. Pour boiling water into blender container. Add gelatin and blend at low speed until dissolved, about 30 seconds.
3. Combine water and ice cubes to make 1 1/4 cups. Add to gelatin and stir until ice is partially melted. Add whipped topping and orange rind and blend at high speed until ice is melted, about 30 seconds.
4. Pour into glasses. Chill until set, about 2 hours.

Serves 6

DIET 7-UP SALAD

Chol: 33 mg   Carbo: 11 gm   Fat: 9 gm
Calories: 152   Protein: 5 gm   Fiber: Tr.
Sodium: 189 mg

INGREDIENTS:

1 1/2 C. crushed pineapple
1 C. hot water
1sm. pkg. lime flavor sugar-free gelatin
1 8 oz. pkg. lite cream cheese
1 pkg. sugar substitute
1 tsp. vanilla
7 oz. diet lemon-lime soda

STEPS IN PREPARATION:

1. Drain pineapple, saving juice. Add enough hot water to juice to equal 1 cup. Bring to a boil.
2. Pour into blender and add gelatin and cheese. Blend on medium speed about 2 minutes. Add sugar substitute, vanilla, and lemon-lime soda. Blend on high speed for 1 minute. Add pineapple and blend on low speed for 1 minute.
3. Pour into dish or mold and chill for 5 hours.

Serves 6

FRUIT JUICE GELATIN

EACH SERVING Amount: 1 portion
Exchanges: 1/2 fruit

Chol: 0   **Carbo:** 7 gm   **Fat:** Tr.
Calories: 37   **Protein:** 1 gm   **Fiber:** Tr.
Sodium: 52 mg

INGREDIENTS:

1sm. pkg. sugar- free gelatin, any flavor
1 C. boiling water
1 C. unsweetened fruit juice

STEPS IN PREPARATION:

1. Dissolve gelatin in boiling water. Add fruit juice and chill in bowl or individual dessert dishes until set, about 2 hours.
Serves 4

Fruit Juice Cubes:
Prepare Fruit Juice Gelatin as directed, reducing boiling water to 3/4 cup. Chill in 9x5 inch loaf pan until firm, about 4 hours, or overnight. Cut into squares.

Suggested Combinations:
Strawberry or lime flavor with orange juice.
Raspberry flavor with apple juice.
Orange, lime or Hawaiian pineapple flavor with canned unsweetened pineapple juice.
Strawberry flavor with grape juice.
Cherry, mixed fruit or lime flavor with white grape juice.
Orange flavor with cranberry juice cocktail.

FRUITY COTTAGE CHEESE

EACH SERVING Amount: 1 portion
Exchanges: 1/2 meat
1/3 fruit
1/2 fat (if whipped topping used)

Chol: Tr.   **Carbo:** 11 gm   **Fat:** 1 gm
Calories: 61   **Protein:** 1 gm   **Fiber:** Tr.
Sodium: 36 mg

INGREDIENTS:

1 sm. pkg. sugar-free gelatin, any flavor
3/4 C. boiling water
1/2 C. cold water
Ice cubes
1 1/2 C. sliced or diced fresh or canned fruit (unsweetened)
3/4 C. low-fat cottage cheese
3/4 C. sugar-free whipped topping (optional)
1 tsp. grated lemon rind (optional)

STEPS IN PREPARATION:

1. Dissolve gelatin in boiling water.
2. Combine cold water and ice cubes to make 1 1/4 cups. Add to gelatin and stir until slightly thickened; remove any unmelted ice. Add fruit.
3. Combine cheese, whipped topping and lemon rind; spoon into individual dessert glasses.
4. Top with the fruited gelatin. Chill until set, about 2 hours.

Serves 6

PISTACHIO DREAM SALAD

EACH SERVING Amount: 1 portion
Exchanges: 1/2 meat
1/2 bread
1/2 fruit
1/2 milk
1 fat

Chol: 3 mg   **Carbo:** 33 gm   **Fat:** 5 gm
Calories: 204 **Protein:** 9 gm   **Fiber:** 2 gm
Sodium: 240 mg

INGREDIENTS:

1 envelope sugar-free whipped topping (mix according to directions except use low-fat milk in place of the water)

1 small can unsweetened mandarin oranges, drained

1 small can unsweetened pineapple, drained

1/2 C. low-fat cottage cheese

1/4 C. unsweetened coconut, optional

1 small box sugar-free pistachio pudding

STEPS IN PREPARATION:

1. Whip topping according to directions using the low-fat milk. Add all other ingredients.
2. The pudding is sprinkled in dry. Mix with mixer just long enough to mix all ingredients. Sprinkle chopped pecans on top if desired.

Serves 4

CRANBERRY-ORANGE SALAD

EACH SERVING Amount: 1 portion
Exchanges: 1/2 fruit

Chol: 0 **Carbo:** 6 gm **Fat:** 1 gm
Calories: 29 **Protein:** 1 gm **Fiber:** 2 gm
Sodium: 34 mg

INGREDIENTS:

1 medium orange
11/2 C. raw cranberries
3 pkg. sugar substitute
1 small pkg. sugar-free gelatin strawberry or
orange flavor
3/4 C. boiling water
1/2 C. cold water
Ice cubes

STEPS IN PREPARATION:

1. Quarter the orange and remove seeds and half of the rind.
2. Combine remaining orange and rind and the cranberries in food processor or food grinder. Chop finely. Add sweetener and set aside.
3. Dissolve gelatin in boiling water. Combine cold water and ice cubes to make 1 1/4 cups. Add to gelatin and stir until slightly thickened; remove any unmelted ice. Add fruit mixture.
4. Pour into 8" square pan or mold and chill until set, about 2 hours. Cut into cubes or spoon onto salad greens.

Serves 6

LAYERED CRANBERRY SALAD

EACH SERVING Amount: 1/2 cup
Exchanges: 1/4 bread
1/2 fat

Chol: Tr.   **Carbo:** 7 gm   **Fat:** 1 gm
Calories: 47   **Protein:** 2 gm   **Fiber:** 1 gm
Sodium: 82 mg

INGREDIENTS:

1 (3 oz.) pkg. sugar-free vanilla pudding (not instant)
1 small pkg. sugar-free lemon gelatin
2 C. water
2 Tbsp. lemon juice
1 small pkg. sugar-free raspberry gelatin
1 C. boiling water
2 C. fresh cranberries
1/2 C. chopped celery
1 pkg. sugar-free whipped topping
1/2 tsp. ground nutmeg
lettuce leaves

STEPS IN PREPARATION:

1. Combine first 3 ingredients in a saucepan; cook over medium heat, stirring constantly, until gelatin dissolves. Stir in lemon juice. Chill until consistency of unbeaten egg white.
2. Dissolve raspberry gelatin in 1 cup boiling water. Stir in cranberries, blend well. Stir in celery. Chill until partially set.

3. Prepare sugar-free whipped topping according to package, adding nutmeg. Fold into lemon gelatin mixture.
4. Spoon 1 1/2 cups mixture into a lightly oiled 7 cup mold. Chill until set.
5. Spoon raspberry gelatin mixture over lemon mixture; chill until set. Spoon remaining lemon mixture over raspberry layer. Chill until firm.
6. Unmold on lettuce leaves.

Serves 12-14

CITRUS BOWL

EACH SERVING Amount: 1 portion
Exchanges: 1/2 fruit

Chol: 0   **Carbo:** 9 gm   **Fat:** Tr.
Calories: 41   **Protein:** 1 gm   **Fiber:** 1 gm
Sodium: 33 mg

INGREDIENTS:

1 sm. pkg. sugar-free gelatin, orange, lemon or Hawaiian-pineapple flavor
3/4 C. boiling water
1 1/4 C. cold club soda
3/4 C. diced grapefruit sections
3/4 C. diced orange sections *
*Or use 1 (11 oz.) can unsweetened mandarin orange sections, drained.

STEPS IN PREPARATION:

1. Dissolve gelatin in boiling water. Add soda and fruits.
2. Chill until set, about 2 hours, stirring after about 15 minutes to distribute fruit.
3. Serve over salad greens.

Serves 6

YOGURT FLUFF

EACH SERVING Amount: 1 portion
Exchanges: 1/4 milk

Chol: 0   **Carbo:** 4 gm   **Fat:** 0
Calories: 37   **Protein:** 4 gm   **Fiber:** 0
Sodium: 91 mg

INGREDIENTS:
3/4 C. boiling water
1 sm. pkg. sugar-free gelatin, any flavor that is red
1/2 C. cold water
Ice cubes
1 (8 oz.) container plain non-fat yogurt
1/2 tsp. vanilla

STEPS IN PREPARATION:
1. Pour boiling water into blender container. Add gelatin and blend at low speed until dissolved, about one minute.
2. Combine cold water and ice cubes to make one cup. Add to gelatin and stir until ice is almost melted, then blend in yogurt and vanilla
3. Chill in dessert glasses or bowl until set, about one hour.
Serves 4

Variation: Tropical Snack
    Substitute 1/2 C. pineapple juice for the water and 1 C. cold skim milk for the yogurt, omitting the vanilla. Garnish with sprinkles of unsweetened flaked coconut.
Serves 4
Exchanges: 1/4 milk   1/4 fruit

VALENTINE'S DAY DELIGHT

EACH SERVING Amount: 1 portion
Exchanges: 1/2 milk

Chol: 2 mg   **Carbo:** 10 gm **Fat:** Tr.
Calories: 59   **Protein:** 5 gm **Fiber:** Tr.
Sodium: 54 mg

INGREDIENTS:

1/4 C. cold water
1 envelope unflavored gelatin
1/2 C. unsweetened pineapple juice
2/3 C. non-fat dry powdered milk
1 tsp. strawberry extract
8 large ice cubes

STEPS IN PREPARATION:

1. In small saucepan, sprinkle gelatin over water. Let stand 1 minute. Add pineaple juice. Stir over low heat until gelatin is completely dissolved. Cool slightly.
2. In blender, combine non-fat milk, and extract and gelatin mixture. Cover. Blend at low speed adding ice cubes one at a time. Then blend on high until mixture thickens and begins to set. Serve immediately.

Serves 4

ZUCCHINI SALAD

EACH SERVING Amount: 1 portion
Exchanges: 1/4 vegetable

Chol: 0   Carbo: 2 gm   Fat: Tr.
Calories: 20   Protein: 2 gm   Fiber: 2 gm
Sodium: 55 mg

INGREDIENTS:

1 small pkg. sugar-free gelatin
    lemon, orange, or lime flavor
1/4 tsp. salt, optional
3/4 C. boiling water
1/4 tsp. oregano (optional)
1 Tbsp. lemon juice
1/2 C. cold water
Ice cubes
1 C. shredded zucchini
1 Tbsp. chopped pimento
1 Tbsp. minced onion

STEPS IN PREPARATION:

1. Dissolve gelatin and salt in boiling water. Add oregano and lemon juice.
2. Combine cold water and ice cubes to make 1-1/4 cups. Add to gelatin and stir until slightly thickened; remove any unmelted ice.
3. Add zucchini, pimiento and onion; pour into bowl. Chill until set, about 2 hours.

Serves 4

Other suggested combinations:
1/2 C. shredded carrots, 1/2 C. shredded cabbage, 1 Tbsp. chopped green pepper.

1 C. shredded cucumbers, 1 Tbsp. chopped olives, 1 Tbsp. minced onion.

GARDEN SALAD

EACH SERVING Amount: 1 portion
Exchanges: 1/2 vegetable

Chol: 0   **Carbo:** 3 gm   **Fat:** Tr.
Calories: 17   **Protein:** 1 gm   **Fiber:** Tr.
Sodium: 131 mg

INGREDIENTS:

1 medium tomato, seeded and chopped (1 C.)
1/2 C. cucumber, diced, seeded, and peeled
1/4 C. chopped green pepper
2 scallions, sliced
2 Tbsp. vinegar
1/4 tsp. salt
Dash of pepper
1 small pkg. sugar-free gelatin, lemon flavor
3/4 C. boiling water
1/2 C. cold water
Ice cubes

STEPS IN PREPARATION:

1. Combine vegetables, vinegar, salt, and pepper; set aside.
2. Dissolve gelatin in boiling water.
3. Combine cold water and ice cubes to make 1 1/4 cups. Add gelatin and stir until slightly thickened; remove any unmelted ice. Add vegetable mixture. Chill or let stand until thickened, about 5 minutes.
4. Pour into bowl and chill until set, at least 30 minutes.

Serves 6

CUCUMBER-DILL SALAD

EACH SERVING Amount: 1 portion
Exchanges: 1/4 vegetable
1/8 milk

Chol: 0   **Carbo:** 3 gm   **Fat:** Tr.
Calories: 26   **Protein:** 3 gm   **Fiber:** Tr.
Sodium: 215 mg

INGREDIENTS:
1 small pkg. lemon or lime sugar-free gelatin
1/4 tsp. salt
3/4 C. boiling water
1 Tbsp. lemon juice
1/2 C. cold water
Ice cubes
1/2 C. plain non-fat yogurt
1 C. cucumber, chopped, seeded, and peeled
1 tsp. dill

STEPS IN PREPARATION:
1. Dissolve gelatin and salt in boiling water. Add lemon juice.
2. Combine cold water and ice cubes to make 1 1/4 cups. Add to gelatin and stir until slightly thickened; remove any unmelted ice. Blend in yogurt; add remaining ingredients.
3. Pour into bowl and chill until firm, about 2 hours.
4. Spoon from bowl onto salad greens.

Serves 4

MIXED VEGETABLE SALAD

EACH SERVING Amount: 1 portion
Exchanges: 1 vegetable

Chol: Tr.　　**Carbo:** 5 gm　**Fat:** Tr.
Calories: 28　**Protein:** 2 gm　**Fiber:** 2 gm
Sodium: 161 mg

INGREDIENTS:

1 small pkg. sugar-free gelatin, lemon flavor
1 chicken bouillon cube
1 C. boiling water
1 (10 oz.) pkg. frozen mixed vegetables
3/4 C. cold water
2 Tbsp. vinegar

STEPS IN PREPARATION:

1. Dissolve gelatin and bouillon cube in boiling water. Add frozen vegetables and stir until thawed and separated. Add cold water and vinegar; chill or let stand until thickened, about 5 minutes.
2. Pour into bowl and chill until set, at least 30 minutes.

Serves 6

VEGETABLES

BREAD & BUTTER PICKLES

EACH SERVING Amount: 1/2 cup
Exchanges: 1 vegetable

Chol: 0   **Carbo:** 8 gm   **Fat:** Tr.
Calories: 34   **Protein:** 2 gm   **Fiber:** 2 gm
Sodium: 389 mg

INGREDIENTS:
4 cucumbers - peeled and sliced thin
1 onion - sliced thin
1 tsp. salt
6 oz. white vinegar
6 oz. tarragon vinegar
1/2 C. water
1 tsp. mustard seed
1/2 tsp. turmeric
4 pkgs. sugar substitute

STEPS IN PREPARATION:
1. In deep dish, layer cucumbers, onions and salt. Place 4 or 5 ice cubes on top, cover with cold water. Cover dish and place in refrigerator for 2 to 3 hours, or overnight.
2. In saucepan, mix 6 oz. white vinegar and 6 oz. terragon vinegar, 1/2 C. water, 1 tsp. mustard seed, 1/2 tsp. celery seed, 1/2 tsp. turmeric, and 4 pkgs. sugar substitute. Mix well. Place over low heat and bring to a boil. Add drained cucumbers, heat, BUT DO NOT BOIL.
3. Place cucumbers in jars and then pour liquid over them. Refrigerate overnight before eating.
Makes about 1 1/2 quarts.

When your cucumbers are gone, slice an apple thin into the juice, refrigerate overnight, and eat for fruit the next day. It's delicious.

LEMON - SESAME ASPARAGUS

EACH SERVING Amount: 1 portion
Exchanges: 1 vegetable
              1/2 fat

Chol: 0   Carbo: 6 gm   Fat: 4 gm
Calories: 64   Protein: 5 gm Fiber: 2 gm
Sodium: 356 mg

INGREDIENTS:
12 oz. fresh asparagus or 1 (8 oz.) package frozen spears
1 Tbsp. diet margarine
1 tsp. sesame seed
2 tsp. lemon juice
1/4 tsp. salt

STEPS IN PREPARATION:
1. Wash and trim fresh asparagus.
2. Cook, covered in boiling, lightly salted water 10-15 minutes or until crisp-tender (cook frozen asparagus according to package directions).
3. In small pan, heat and stir margarine and sesame seed over low heat for five minutes or until seeds are golden brown. Add lemon juice and salt.
4. Drain asparagus, remove to heated serving dish.
5. Pour lemon mixture over hot asparagus and serve immediately.

Serves 2.

SWEET 'N SOUR BEETS

EACH SERVING Amount: 1 portion
Exchanges: 1 vegetable
1/2 fat

Chol: 0   **Carbo:** 6 gm   **Fat:** 5 gm
Calories: 52   **Protein:** 1 gm   **Fiber:** Tr.
Sodium: 76 mg

INGREDIENTS:
1 tsp. sugar substitute
1/2 Tbsp. cornstarch
1/4 C. mild vinegar
1/4 C. water
1 C. small beets, sliced or cubed (drained)
2 Tbsp. diet margarine

STEPS IN PREPARATION:
1. Mix sugar substitute and cornstarch. Add vinegar and water and boil 1 minute. Add beets and let stand at least 30 minutes.
2. Just before serving, bring to boiling point and add diet margarine.

Serves 4.

STIR - FRY BROCCOLI

EACH SERVING Amount: 1/2 cup
Exchanges: 1 vegetable

Chol: Tr.   **Carbo:** 3 gm   **Fat:** 1 gm
Calories: 24   **Protein:** 2 gm **Fiber:** 1 gm
Sodium: 198 mg

INGREDIENTS:
1 lb. fresh broccoli
1/2 C. boiling water
4 lemon slices
1 tsp. vegetable oil
1/2 tsp. chicken flavored bouillon

STEPS IN PREPARATION:
1. Trim off large leaves of broccoli. Remove rough ends of lower stalks. Separate into spears.
2. Heat oil in a large non-stick skillet over medium-high heat until hot. Add broccoli, stir-fry 1 minute.
3. Combine water and bouillon, stirring well. Add broccoli. Cover and cook 3 minutes or until crisp-tender.
4. Garnish with lemon slices to serve.

Serves 6

BROCCOLI WITH MUSTARD-DILL SAUCE

EACH SERVING Amount: 1/2 cup broccoli with1 Tbsp. sauce

Exchanges: 1 vegetable
1/4 fat

Chol: Tr.   **Carbo:** 7 gm   **Fat:** 3 gm
Calories: 54   **Protein:** 3 gm   **Fiber:** 3 gm
Sodium: 204 mg

INGREDIENTS:

Fresh broccoli spears
1/2 C. water with 1/4 tsp. salt
1 Tbsp. diet margarine
1/4 tsp. salt
1/4 tsp. dill
1 Tbsp. flour
1 1/2 tsp. prepared mustard
1/2 C. skim milk

STEPS IN PREPARATION:

1. Bring fresh broccoli and salted water to boil; cover and cook until just tender, about 6 minutes. (Cook frozen broccoli as directed.)
2. Melt diet margarine; add flour and cook about 1 minute, stirring constantly. Add salt, dill, mustard and milk. Stir until smooth; bring to a simmer; cook 2 minutes while stirring constantly.

Serves 4

BRUSSELS SPROUTS IN MUSHROOM SAUCE

EACH SERVING Amount: 1 portion
Exchanges: 1/4 bread
                  1 vegetable
                  1 fat

Chol: 2 mg   **Carbo:** 16 gm **Fat:** 6 gm
Calories: 93 **Protein:** 6 gm **Fiber:** 3 gm
Sodium: 1247 mg

INGREDIENTS:
2 C. brussels sprouts
1 (10 3/4 oz.) can mushroom soup
1/2 C. skim evaporated milk
1 tsp. salt

STEPS IN PREPARATION:
1. Parboil brussels sprouts for 10 minutes.
2. Mix soup and milk together, then heat. Add the brussels sprouts and simmer until tender, about 10-15 minutes.
Serves 4.

BRAISED CELERY AND MUSHROOMS

EACH SERVING Amount: 1 portion
Exchanges: 1 vegetable

Chol: Tr.   **Carbo:** 4 gm   **Fat:** Tr.
Calories: 22   **Protein:** 1 gm   **Fiber:** 1 gm
Sodium: 337 mg

INGREDIENTS:

2 C. diagonally sliced celery
4 oz. mushroom pieces, drained
1/4 C. chopped onion
1 chicken bouillon cube
1 C. boiling water
1/2 tsp. Worcestershire Sauce

STEPS IN PREPARATION:

1. Place celery in large skillet. Scatter mushrooms and onions on top.
2. Dissolve bouillon in water; add sauce and stir. Pour on top of vegetables. Bring to a boil, cover, reduce heat, and simmer 10 minutes, or until celery is crisp-tender.

Serves 4.

ORANGE GLAZED CARROTS

EACH SERVING Amount: 1 portion
Exchanges: 1 vegetable
1/3 fruit
1/3 fat

Chol: 0   **Carbo:** 12 gm   **Fat:** 2 gm
Calories: 66   **Protein:** Tr.   **Fiber:** 1 gm
Sodium: 248 mg

INGREDIENTS:
3 C. sliced carrots
1/2 C. water
1/2 tsp. salt
1/2 C. unsweetened orange juice
1 Tbsp. cornstarch
2 Tbsp. diet margarine
1 medium orange, diced or sectioned

STEPS IN PREPARATION:
1. Bring salted water to boil. Add carrots, cover and cook until barely tender. Drain the liquid into measuring cup. Remove carrots from pan.
2. In saucepan, mix liquids with cornstarch. Cook on medium heat, stirring constantly, until thickened and clear. Add margarine, carrots, and orange; heat through.

Serves 6.

SWEET AND SOUR CARROTS

EACH SERVING Amount: 1 portion
Exchanges: 1/4 bread
               1 vegetable
               1/2 fat

Chol: 0   Carbo: 12 gm   Fat: 1 gm
Calories: 86   Protein: 163 gm   Fiber: 2 gm
Sodium: 416 mg

INGREDIENTS:

1/2 C. green pepper, cut into squares
1 medium clove garlic, minced
1 Tbsp. diet margarine
1 Tomato Nestle Souptime, prepared
1 Tbsp. water
2 tsp. vinegar
2 C. diagonally sliced, cooked carrots
1 pkg. sugar substitute
Parsley for garnish (optional)

STEPS IN PREPARATION:

1. Saute green pepper with garlic in 1 tsp. diet margarine until tender. Add remaining ingredients except sugar substitute.
2. Simmer about 20 minutes stirring occasionally.
3. When ready to serve, sprinkle on the sugar substitute and stir. Garnish with parsley.

Serves 4

CAULIFLOWER ITALIANO

EACH SERVING Amount: 1 portion
Exchanges: 1/2 vegetable

Chol: 0   Carbo: 5 gm   Fat: 1 gm
Calories: 26   Protein: 1 gm Fiber: 2 gm
Sodium: 206 mg

INGREDIENTS:

1 Tbsp. chopped onion
1 small clove garlic, minced
2 Tbsp. low-calorie Italian dressing
3 C. small fresh cauliflowerettes
1/4 C. water
2 Tbsp. chopped green pepper
1C. cherry tomatoes, halved, or 1 large tomato,
    cut into eighths
1/2 tsp. salt
1/8 tsp. dried basil, crushed

STEPS IN PREPARATION:

1. Cook onion and garlic in salad dressing in
   skillet until tender. Add cauliflowerettes and
   1/4 C. water. Cook covered over low heat 10
   minutes. Add green pepper; cook until
   cauliflower is tender, about 5 minutes.
2. Stir in remaining ingredients. Cook until heated
   through.
Serves 8

CHEESY BEAN CASSEROLE

EACH SERVING Amount: 1 portion
Exchanges: 1/2 meat
               1/4 vegetable
               1/4 bread

Chol: 5 mg   Carbo: 8 gm   Fat: 2 gm
Calories: 65 Protein: 6 gm Fiber: 3 gm
Sodium: 657 mg

INGREDIENTS:

1 (16 oz.) can green beans
1/2 C. skim milk
2 oz. grated low-fat American cheese
1 slice bread, crumbled

STEPS IN PREPARATION:

1. Warm beans. Drain off liquid and put beans into 1 quart casserole.
2. Heat milk, add cheese and bread crumbs, stirring until cheese melts. Pour over green beans.
3. Bake for 15 minutes at 350 degrees.
Serves 4.

GREEN BEAN CASSEROLE

EACH SERVING Amount: 1/2 cup
Exchanges: 1/2 meat
               1 vegetable
               1/2 fat

Chol: 81 mg   Carbo: 6 gm   Fat: 2 gm
Calories: 59   Protein: 5 gm   Fiber: 2 gm
Sodium: 382 mg

INGREDIENTS:
1 (10 oz.) pkg. frozen chopped spinach
1 (9 oz.) pkg. frozen green beans
1/2 C. chopped onion
1/4 C. water
1 tsp. salt
1/8 tsp. garlic powder
1tsp. dried basil
1/8 tsp. nutmeg
1/8 tsp. pepper
3 eggs, beaten
1 oz. grated low-fat American cheese
paprika

STEPS IN PREPARATION:
1. Thaw and drain spinach and green beans.
   Combine with onion, water, salt, garlic powder,
   basil, nutmeg, and pepper. Cover and simmer
   for 10 minutes, stirring occasionally. Remove
   from heat.
2. Gradually stir vegetable mixture into beaten
   eggs. Stir mixture well. Turn into 8 inch baking
   dish.

3. Bake uncovered at 350 degrees for about 20 minutes (or bake until set). Place cheese on top and sprinkle with paprika. Bake for 2-3 minutes more before serving.
Serves 8.

SQUASH WITH PECANS

EACH SERVING Amount: 1 portion
Exchanges: 1 vegetable
1 fat

Chol: 0   **Carbo:** 7 gm   **Fat:** 5 gm
Calories: 68   **Protein:** 2 gm   **Fiber:** 3 gm
Sodium: 786 mg

INGREDIENTS:

4 C. cooked squash
1/4 C. chopped pecans, divided
2 tsp. salt
2 Tbsp. diet margarine, divided
1 1/2 tsp. sugar substitute
1/4 tsp. nutmeg

STEPS IN PREPARATION:

1. Spray 1 1/2 quart casserole with non-stick spray, add squash, stir in 2 Tbsp. diet margarine, 1/4 cup pecans, the sugar substitute, salt, and nutmeg. Sprinkle with remaining pecans. Dot with diet margarine.
2. Bake at 350 degrees for 20-30 minutes.

Serves 6.

CHEESY TOMATOES

EACH SERVING **Amount:** 1 portion
Exchanges: 1 vegetable
1/2 meat

Chol: 1 mg   **Carbo:** 7 gm   **Fat:** 1 gm
Calories: 45   **Protein:** 5 gm   **Fiber:** 1 gm
Sodium: 313 mg

INGREDIENTS:

2 C. cherry tomatoes or plum tomatoes (1 lb.)
1/2 C. low-fat cottage cheese
1 green onion, chopped fine
dash of Worcestershire sauce
garlic salt and pepper to taste

STEPS IN PREPARATION:

1. Cut off tops of tomatoes and scoop out pulp.
2. Combine pulp, cottage cheese, onion, Worcestershire sauce and seasonings; mix well.
3. Pile mixture into shells. Garnish with parsley sprigs or thin slices of green or black olives. Chill well.

Serves 4.

EGGPLANT AND CHEESE PUFF

EACH SERVING Amount: 1 portion
Exchanges: 11/4 meat
              11/2 bread
              11/4 vegetable
              1/2 fat

Chol: 110 mg **Carbo:** 31 gm **Fat:** 6 gm
Calories: 217 **Protein:** 11 gm **Fiber:** 3 gm
Sodium: 505 mg

INGREDIENTS:

2 C. peeled, diced eggplant
1 C. canned, drained garbanzo beans
1/3 C. chopped onion
1 Tbsp. chili powder
1/4 tsp. salt
1/4 tsp. pepper
1 Tbsp. diet margarine
1/2 C. flour
1/2 C. skim milk
2 eggs, lightly beaten
1 oz. shredded low-fat cheddar cheese
1 medium unpeeled tomato, cut into 12 wedges

STEPS IN PREPARATION:

1. Coat a large non-stick skillet with cooking spray; heat until hot. Add eggplant, beans, and onion; saute 5 minutes. Stir in chili powder, salt and pepper; remove from heat and set aside.
2. Coat a 9" pie plate with non-stick cooking spray; add diet margarine.

3. Bake at 475 degrees until margarine melts.
4. Combine flour, milk and eggs. Pour mixture into pie plate-do not stir.
5. Bake at 475 degrees for 12 minutes or until golden brown.
6. poon eggplant mixture over baked cake mixture; bake an additional 2 mintues.
7. Remove and sprinkle with cheese. Let melt and top with tomato wedges.

Serves 4.

BAKED EGGPLANT

EACH SERVING **Amount:** 1 portion
Exchanges: 1 meat
1/2 bread
1 vegetable
1/2 fat

Chol: 113 mg **Carbo:** 15 gm **Fat:** 7 gm
Calories: 163 **Protein:** 10 gm **Fiber:** 2 gm
Sodium: 1181 mg

INGREDIENTS:
16 oz. eggplant, peeled
9 Tbsp. dried bread crumbs
1/2 C. evaporated skim milk
1/4 C. skim milk
3 Tbsp. diet margarine, melted
1/4 C. onion, finely chopped
1/4 C. celery, finely chopped
1/4 C. green peppers, finely chopped
3 eggs, slightly beaten
1 Tbsp. pimiento, chopped
2 tsp. salt
1/2 tsp. pepper
1/4 tsp. sage
3 oz. grated low-fat block cheese

STEPS IN PREPARATION:
1. Cut peeled eggplant into 1-inch cubes and soak in salt water in refrigerator overnight (minimum of 6 hours).
2. Drain eggplant and place in pan. Cover with water and simmer until tender.
3. Soak bread crumbs in milk.
4. Saute onions, green peppers, and celery in

melted margarine for about 15 minutes or until tender.
5. Combine cooked eggplant, bread crumbs, and sauteed vegetables. Add eggs, pimiento, and seasonings; blend thoroughly.
6. Place in greased baking dish and bake at 350 degrees for 45 minutes. Top with grated cheese and return to oven until cheese melts.
Serves 6

VIRGINIA MIXED VEGETABLES

EACH SERVING Amount: 1 portion
Exchanges: 1/2 meat
1 vegetable
1/2 fat
1/4 bread

Chol: 11 mg   **Carbo:** 9 gm   **Fat:** 5 gm
Calories: 108 **Protein:** 7 gm **Fiber:** 2 gm
Sodium: 550 mg

INGREDIENTS:

1 pkg. frozen mixed vegetables, thawed
1/2 C. non-fat yogurt
1/2 C. lite sour cream
1 (10 3/4) can cream of chicken soup
4 oz. grated low-fat cheddar cheese

STEPS IN PREPARATION:

1. Mix all of the above ingredients. Put into a 9 X 13 pan.
2. Bake at 350 degrees for 30 minutes. (If vegetables are thawed you may reduce the baking time.)

Serves 8

SAUTEED ZUCCHINI

EACH SERVING Amount: 1/2 cup
Exchanges: 1 vegetable

Chol: 1 mg   Carbo: 5 gm   Fat: 2 gm
Calories: 39   Protein: 3 gm   Fiber: 3 gm
Sodium: 282 mg

INGREDIENTS:

1/2 C. chopped onion
1 Tbsp. diet margarine
3 1/2 C. sliced zucchini
1 C. sliced fresh mushrooms
1/4 C. chopped red bell pepper
1/2 tsp. salt
1/4 tsp. thyme
1/4 tsp. pepper
1 oz. grated low-fat process American cheese

STEPS IN PREPARATION:

1. Saute onion in margarine in non-stick skillet until tender. You may need to add a small amount of water or broth. Add zucchini, mushrooms, salt, thyme, and pepper.
2. Cook over low heat for 5-7 minutes, stirring often. Zucchini should be tender-crisp. Sprinkle with cheese and serve.

Serves 6.

ZUCCHINI WITH TOMATO AND CHEESE

EACH SERVING Amount: 1/2 cup
Exchanges: 1 vegetable
1/2 fat

Chol: 2 mg   **Carbo:** 4 gm   **Fat:** 2 gm
Calories: 45   **Protein:** 3 gm   **Fiber:** 2 gm
Sodium: 304 mg

INGREDIENTS:

3 C. zucchini, sliced

1 onion, chopped

1 Tbsp. vegetable oil

1 tsp. salt

2 oz. shredded low-fat cheese

1 C. canned tomatoes

STEPS IN PREPARATION:

1. Brown zucchini and onion in oil,cover and simmer 10 minutes.
2. Add rest of ingredients and heat until cheese melts.

Serves 8.

WINTER VEGETABLE STUFFING

EACH SERVING Amount: 1/2 cup
Exchanges: 1 vegetable
              1/3 fat

Chol: 0   **Carbo:** 4 gm   **Fat:** 5 gm
Calories: 58   **Protein:** 1 gm **Fiber:** 2 gm
Sodium: 105 mg

INGREDIENTS:

6 Tbsp. diet margarine
4 celery stalks, sliced
2 red bell peppers
2 small onions, diced
1 medium-sized rutabaga (1-1/2 lb.)
1 lb. mushrooms, sliced
1 (6 oz.) pkg. radishes, sliced
1 tsp. poultry seasoning
Salt to taste
1/2 tsp. Worcestershire sauce

STEPS IN PREPARATION:

1. Combine all ingredients in 8 quart Dutch oven. Cook until tender, spoon into bowl.
2. In the same Dutch oven, over high heat, combine 2 cups water and 2 chicken flavor bouillon cubes, heat until boiling. Add 1 medium size rutabaga (1-1/2 lb.) peeled and shredded. Return to boil. Reduce heat to low. Cover and simmer for 25 minutes or until tender, drain.
3. Return vegetables to Dutch oven, add 1/2 tsp. Worcestershire sauce, 1 tsp. poultry seasoning, and salt to taste; mix well.
4. Cook over medium heat until hot. Put in baking dish to serve.

Serves 8

PASTA, RICE
& STARCHY VEGETABLES

HERB-STUFFED POTATOES

EACH SERVING Amount: 1/2 potato
Exchanges: 1 bread
1/2 fat

Chol: Tr.   Carbo: 21 gm Fat: 2 gm
Calories: 112 Protein: 3 gm Fiber: 2 gm
Sodium: 62 mg

INGREDIENTS:

4 med. baking potatoes (about 4 1/2 inches long)
8 tsp. diet margarine
1 (5 1/3 oz.) can evaporated skim milk
1 tsp. snipped chives
1 tsp. snipped parsley
1/8 tsp. dried sage
salt and pepper to taste
dash paprika

STEPS IN PREPARATION:

1. Preheat oven to 400 degrees.
2. Bake potatoes about 45 minutes. Cut in half lengthwise. Scoop out inside and mash. Add remaining ingredients except paprika. Mix thoroughly. Spoon potato into shells on baking sheet. Sprinkle with paprika.
3. Return to oven for 10 minutes or until lightly browned.

Serves 8

SOUTHERN SWEET POTATO BAKE

EACH SERVING Amount: 1 portion
Exchanges: 1 bread
1/2 fat

Chol: 13 mg Carbo: 12 gm Fat: 4 gm
Calories: 85 Protein: 1 gm Fiber: 1 gm
Sodium: 179 mg

INGREDIENTS:

4 medium sweet potatoes (3 lbs.)

1 tsp. vegetable oil

1 egg, beaten

1 (8 oz.) can crushed pineapple, drained (in own juice)

1 1/3 Tbsp. brown sugar substitute

1/2 C. chopped pecans

4 Tbsp. diet margarine

1 tsp. salt

1 tsp. ground cinnamon

2 Tbsp. grated orange rind

1/2 tsp. vanilla extract

STEPS IN PREPARATION:

1. Wash sweet potatoes and rub potatoes with vegetable oil.
2. Bake at 375 degrees for 1 hour or until done.
3. Slice away skin from top of each potato; carefully scoop out pulp, leaving shells intact. Mash pulp; add remaining ingredients and mix well. Spoon potato mixture into shells. Place on baking sheet.
4. Bake at 375 degrees for 20 minutes.

Serves 16.

ORANGE GLAZED SWEET POTATOES

EACH SERVING Amount: 1 portion
Exchanges: 1 bread
                  1/2 fruit

Chol: 0   **Carbo:** 21 gm   **Fat:** 1 gm
Calories: 92   **Protein:** 2 gm   **Fiber:** 3 gm
Sodium: 56 mg

INGREDIENTS:

2 2/3 C. cooked sweet potatoes
1 Tbsp. diet margarine
3 oranges, peeled and cut into small pieces
1/4 C. orange juice
1/8 tsp. salt
1/4 tsp. pepper
1/4 tsp. ginger

STEPS IN PREPARATION:

1. Preheat oven to 400 degrees.
2. Peel potatoes. Bake one hour or until tender.
3. Mash sweet potatoes and oranges pieces. Add 1/4 C. orange juice, margarine, salt, pepper, and ginger. Stir.
4. Put into greased casserole dish and bake for 15 minutes or until heated.

Serves 8.

SWEET POTATO MUFFINS

EACH SERVING Amount: 2 muffins
Exchanges: 1/4 meat
1/2 bread
1/4 fruit
1/4 milk

Chol: 19 mg **Carbo:** 18 gm **Fat:** 2 gm
Calories: 129 **Protein:** 8 gm **Fiber:** 2 gm
Sodium: 249 mg

INGREDIENTS:

6 slices lite bread
2 eggs + 4 egg whites
2 Tbsp. brown sugar substitute
4 pkg. sugar substitute
1 1/2 tsp. soda
3 tsp. vanilla
2/3 C. baked sweet potato, mashed
6 Tbsp. raisins
6 walnuts, chopped (optional)
1 1/3 C. non-fat dry powdered milk
1 1/2 tsp. cinnamon
1 1/2 tsp. nutmeg

STEPS IN PREPARATION:

1. Blend all ingredients in blender. Pour into muffin tins that have been sprayed with non-stick spray.
2. Bake at 350 degrees for 20 minutes. You can substitute 1 1/2 cups pumpkin in the place of sweet potato.

Yields 24

PUMPKIN CORN MUFFINS

EACH SERVING Amount: 1 muffin
Exchanges: 3/4 bread

Chol: 12 mg   **Carbo:** 9 gm   **Fat:** 2 gm
Calories: 60   **Protein:** 2 gm   **Fiber:** 2 gm
Sodium: 92 mg

INGREDIENTS:
1 C. whole wheat flour
1 C. cornmeal
1 1/2 Tbsp. baking powder
1/2 tsp. baking soda
optional: pinch of salt
1 egg
1 C. low-fat buttermilk
1/2 C. cooked or canned plain pumpkin
1/4 C. sugar-free jam
2 Tbsp. safflower oil

STEPS IN PREPARATION:
1. Thoroughly mix flour, corn meal, baking powder, baking soda and salt; set aside.
2. Beat egg lightly; then beat in buttermilk, pumpkin, jam and oil. Combine dry and wet ingredients thoroughly. Divide dough among 18 non-stick muffin cups, sprayed with non-stick cooking spray.
3. Bake in a preheated 425 degree oven 20-25 minutes until muffins test done.
Yields 18

FRENCH GREEN PEAS

EACH SERVING Amount: 1 portion
Exchanges: 1 bread
1/2 fat

Chol: 0   **Carbo:** 17 gm   **Fat:** 3 gm
Calories: 117   **Protein:** 6 gm   **Fiber:** 8 gm
Sodium: 215 mg

INGREDIENTS:
1 head Boston or 1/2 medium-size head Iceberg
    lettuce
2 Tbsp. diet margarine
1/4 C. water
1/4 tsp. salt
1 small yellow onion, peeled and chopped
2 C. fresh or frozen green peas
1 Tbsp. chopped fresh or 1 tsp. dried parsley

STEPS IN PREPARATION:
1. Discard core and outer leaves of lettuce and slice lettuce into very thin shreds.
2. Place margarine, water and salt in 2-quart saucepan. Top with lettuce, onion and peas. Sprinkle with parsley and cover. Bring to a boil, then lower heat and simmer about 10 minutes (5 minutes if using frozen peas), or until peas are tender.
3. Spoon peas, along with juices, into individual dishes.

Serves 4.

OAT PILAF

Chol: Tr.   Carbo: 18 gm Fat: Tr.
Calories: 174 Protein: 7 gm Fiber: 2 gm
Sodium: 213 mg

INGREDIENTS:

1 Tbsp. diet margarine
1/2 C. fresh mushrooms, sliced
1/2 C. red pepper, chopped
1/2 C. onion, chopped
1/2 C. celery, chopped
2 egg whites
1 3/4 C. quick cooking oats
1 C. chicken bouillon

STEPS IN PREPARATION:

1. Melt margarine in skillet over medium heat. Add vegetables and saute 2 to 3 minutes.
2. In a separate bowl, mix oats and egg whites until oats are coated. Add oats to vegetable mixture and cook 5 minutes or until lightly browned. Add broth and continue cooking until liquid is absorbed.

Serves 8.

PINTO BEANS A LA JUAN

EACH SERVING Amount: 1/2 cup
Exchanges: 1 bread
1 vegetable

Chol: 141   **Carbo:** 30 gm   **Fat:** 1 gm
Calories: 141   **Protein:** 9 gm   **Fiber:** 17 gm
Sodium: 1236 mg

INGREDIENTS:
2 lbs. pinto beans rinsed
10 qts. water
6 whole garlic cloves (discard after 2 hrs. cooking)
1 lg. onion chopped medium coarse
1 heaping Tbsp. chili powder
2 heaping Tbsp. Tony's Creole Seasoning
1 heaping Tbsp. Goya Adobo
1 heaping Tbsp. salt

STEPS IN PREPARATION:
Mix all ingredients. In 3 gallon pot, boil gently 1 1/2 hours and taste for seasoning. Cook 5 hours total on low rolling boil.

For Cilantro Beans:
When beans are tender add:
2 medium bell pepper, chopped medium coarse
4 firm tomatoes chopped medium coarse
1 large yellow onion chopped coarse
1 bunch cilantro rinsed and tied (discard cilantro after beans are done)

SAUCES / DIPS

BASIC WHITE SAUCE

EACH SERVING Amount: 1 portion
Exchanges:　　1/4 bread
　　　　　　　　1/4 milk
　　　　　　　　1/2 fat

Chol: 1 mg　　Carbo: 6 gm　　Fat: 3 gm
Calories: 50　　Protein: 3 gm　　Fiber: Tr.
Sodium: 374 mg

INGREDIENTS:
　2 Tbsp. diet margarine
　2 Tbsp. flour
　1/2 tsp. salt (opt.)
　1 C. skim milk

STEPS IN PREPARATION:
　1. Melt margarine in medium saucepan. Add flour and stil until all flour is coated evenly with margarine. Stir in salt. Slowly add milk, stirring constantly. Heat sauce to boiling, stirring frequently. Cook 1 minute to thicken.
　2. This sauce can be added to casseroles or used as a base for soups and sauces or as a cream sauce over vegetables.
Serves 4

HELP YOUR HEART SOUR CREAM

EACH SERVING Amount: 1/2 Tbsp. = free
Exchanges: 1/4 c. = 1/2 meat

Chol: 2 mg   Carbo: 2 gm   Fat: Tr.
Calories: 40   Protein: 7 gm   Fiber: Tr.
Sodium: 185 mg

INGREDIENTS:

1 C. low-fat cottage cheese
2 tsp. lemon juice

STEPS IN PREPARATION:

Place ingredients in blender for 20 seconds. Use in any recipe that calls for sour cream. May be added to hot dishes at the last moment.

VEGETABLE DIP

EACH SERVING Amount: 4 Tbsp.
   Exchanges: 1 fat
       1/4 milk

Chol: 0 **Carbo:** 4 gm **Fat:** 8 gm
Calories: 96 **Protein:** 1 gm **Fiber:** 0
Sodium: 437 mg

INGREDIENTS:
1 C. low-fat mayonnaise
1 C. plain non-fat yogurt
1 1/2 tsp. celery seed
1 tsp. dill weed
1 tsp. parsley flakes
1 tsp. garlic salt

STEPS IN PREPARATION:
Mix well, gradually adding spices to taste.

SPICY TACO DIP

EACH SERVING Amount: 1/4 cup
Exchanges: 1/4 milk

Chol: 0   **Carbo:** 5 gm   **Fat:** 0 gm
Calories: 36   **Protein:** 3 gm   **Fiber:** Tr.
Sodium: 105 mg

INGREDIENTS:

1 C. plain non-fat yogurt
3 Tbsp. tomato paste
1/2 to 1 tsp. dry mustard
1/8 to 1/4 tsp. chili powder
1 tsp. chopped onion

STEPS IN PREPARATION:

Combine yogurt and tomato paste and blend well. Mix in remaining ingredients. Refrigerate for a few hours. Serve with vegetables or taco chips.

YOGURT CHEESE

Chol: 0   Carbo: 4 gm   Fat: 0
Calories: 28   Protein: 3 gm   Fiber: 0
Sodium: 40 mg

INGREDIENTS:
1 (8 oz.) carton plain non-fat yogurt

STEPS IN PREPARATION:
Place yogurt in a funnel lined with a coffee filter to allow whey to drain from yogurt overnight in the refrigerator. Use as sour cream.
Serves 4

Variations:
Substitute for Sour Cream or Cream Cheese
Add sugar substitute and vanilla to use as
    icing.
Add garlic, salt, chives for baked potatoes.

SPINACH DIP

EACH SERVING Amount: 1/4 cup
Exchanges: 1/4 vegetable
                   1/4 milk

Chol: 0   **Carbo:** 5 gm   **Fat:** Tr.
Calories: 31   **Protein:** 3 gm **Fiber:** 2 gm
Sodium: 56 mg

INGREDIENTS:

1 stalk (bunch) fresh celery
1 (10 oz.) pkg. frozen chopped spinach, defrosted
1 (8 oz.) container plain low-fat yogurt
1/2 tsp. dry Italian seasoning, crushed
1/4 tsp. garlic powder

STEPS IN PREPARATION:

1. Remove leaves from celery; cut ribs into 4-1 to 2 inch lengths. Place in a bowl and cover with cold water; refrigerate until ready to serve.
2. Place spinach in sieve and press out as much liquid as possible.
3. In medium bowl, combine spinach, yogurt, Italian seasoning, garlic powder. Cover and refrigerate until ready to serve.
4. Spoon into a serving bowl. Serve with celery sticks.

Serves 6

DIP FOR VEGETABLES

Chol: 2 mg **Carbo:** 7 gm **Fat:** 2 gm
Calories: 41 **Protein:** 7 gm **Fiber:** 0
Sodium: 187 mg

INGREDIENTS:
1 (16 oz.) carton low-fat (2% or less) cottage
cheese
1/2 packet Hidden Valley Ranch Original
seasoning mix
2 Tbsp. skim milk

STEPS IN PREPARATION:
Blend in blender until smooth. Use as a dip for
celery, carrots, cucumber, raw cauliflower, green
pepper, etc.

Thin with more skim milk and use as a high
protein salad dressing.

CUCUMBER DIP

EACH SERVING Amount: 1/2 cup
Exchanges: 1/2 milk
2 Tbsp = free

Chol: 0   Carbo: 7 gm   Fat: Tr.
Calories: 40   Protein: 3 gm   Fiber: Tr.
Sodium: 42 mg

INGREDIENTS:

1 C. plain non-fat yogurt
1 large cucumber, peeled, seeded, and cut into
  small pieces
1/2 small onion or 3 green onions cut into pieces
dash of freshly ground pepper.

STEPS IN PREPARATION:

Combine all ingredients in blender and whirl until
well blended. Pour into a bowl and refrigerate for
several hours or overnight.

CHOCOLATE SYRUP

EACH SERVING Amount: 2 Tbsp.
Exchanges: 2 Tbsp. = free

Chol: 2 mg   **Carbo:** 3 gm   **Fat:** Tr.
Calories: 17   **Protein:** 1 gm   **Fiber:** Tr.
Sodium: 114 mg

INGREDIENTS:
1/2 C. cocoa, packed
1 1/4 C. cold water
1/4 tsp. salt
2 1/2 tsp. vanilla
sugar substitute to equal 1/2 C. sugar

STEPS IN PREPARATION:
1. Bring cocoa, water and salt to boil, simmer for 3 minutes.
2. Cool 10 minutes and add sugar substitute to equal 1/2 C. sugar. Add vanilla.

DESSERTS

BLUEBERRY CRISP

EACH SERVING Amount: 1/2 cup
Exchanges: 1 bread
1/2 fruit
1/2 fat

Chol: 0   **Carbo:** 22 gm   **Fat:** 4 gm
Calories: 125   **Protein:** 1 gm   **Fiber:** 3 gm
Sodium: 273 mg

INGREDIENTS:
4 C. fresh or frozen blueberries (unsweetened)
12 pkgs. sugar substitute
2 2/3 C. cold water
2 tsp. lemon juice
1/2 tsp. salt
4 Tbsp. cornstarch (dissolve in 4 Tbsp. water)
7-3oz. large shredded wheat biscuits, crumbled
1/2 C. brown sugar substitute
4 Tbsp. diet margarine, melted
4 Tbsp. liquid butter flavoring
sugar-free whipped topping, opt. (2 tsp. free)

STEPS IN PREPARATION:
1. Preheat oven to 350 degrees.
2. In a small saucepan, cook blueberries with sweetener, water, lemon juice, and salt. Stir in cornstarch mixture. Pour into bottom of 9 X 13 baking dish.
3. Mix biscuit crumbs, brown sugar substitute, margarine, and liquid butter flavoring. Sprinkle evenly over berry mixture; bake for about 25 minutes, or until mixture is bubbly.
4. Serve plain or with sugar-free whipped topping. Serves 8.

COBBLER - CHERRY, APPLE, BLUEBERRY, PINEAPPLE

EACH SERVING Amount: 1/2 cup
Exchanges: 1 bread
2 fruit
1/2 milk

Chol: 5 mg **Carbo:** 47 gm **Fat:** Tr
Calories: 231 **Protein:** 10 gm **Fiber:** 4 gm
Sodium: 444 mg

INGREDIENTS:

2 servings of fresh fruit (cherry, apple, blueberry or pineapple)
1/2 pkg. sugar substitute
3 Tbsp. non-fat dry powdered milk
2 1/2 Tbsp. flour
Pinch of salt
3/4 tsp. baking powder
3 Tbsp. water

STEPS IN PREPARATION:

1. Put fruit into an oven dish. Sprinkle with 1/2 package of sugar substitute. Add 1 Tbsp. water. Stir to mix.
2. Combine remaining ingredients, stir until smooth and pour over fruit mixture.
3. Bake at 400 degrees for 25 to 35 minutes. Serves 1.

PEACH COBBLER

EACH SERVING **Amount:** 1 slice
Exchanges: 3/4 bread
1/2 fruit
1/2 fat

Chol: Tr.　　**Carbo:** 22 gm　**Fat:** 3 gm
Calories: 121　**Protein:** 2 gm　**Fiber:** 2 gm
Sodium: 375 mg

INGREDIENTS:

3 C. canned peaches (water packed) or 4 C.
　sliced fresh peaches
1 C. flour
1 Tbsp. baking powder
1/2 tsp. salt
1/2 C. juice from peaches; 1/2 C. skim milk if
　using fresh fruit
4 Tbsp. diet margarine

STEPS IN PREPARATION:

1. Melt margarine in bottom of baking dish.
2. Mix flour, baking powder, salt, and liquid in a
　separate bowl. Pour batter on the melted butter.
3. Spoon peaches on the batter; bake at 350
　degrees for 30 minutes.
Serves 8.

CRANBERRY COBBLER

EACH SERVING **Amount:** 1 portion
Exchanges: 1 bread
             2 fruits
             1 fat

Chol: Tr.   **Carbo:** 66 gm   **Fat:** 5 gm
Calories: 297   **Protein:** 5 gm   **Fiber:** 7 gm
Sodium: 330 mg

INGREDIENTS:
   FILLING:
      2 C. raisins
      2 C. fresh or frozen cranberries
      3 Tbsp. sugar substitute
      2 tsp. cornstarch
      1/2 tsp. ground allspice
      1 C. orange juice
   TOPPING:
      1 C. flour
      2 tsp. baking powder
      1/4 tsp. salt
      1/4 C. diet margarine
      1/2 C. skim milk
      ground cinnamon
      2 pkgs. sugar substitute

STEPS IN PREPARATION:
   1. Filling - In medium saucepan, combine raisins, cranberries, sugar substitute, cornstarch, and allspice. Gradually stir in orange juice. Bring to boil over high heat; reduce heat to low and simmer, stirring until cranberries begin to pop and mixture thickens slightly. Pour into shallow 1 1/2 quart baking dish.

2. In small bowl, combine flour, baking powder, and salt. Cut in diet margarine until mixture resembles coarse meal. Mix in milk lightly with fork.
3. Drop spoonfuls of batter over filling; sprinkle lightly with sugar substitute mixed with cinnamon.
4. Bake in preheated 400 degree oven about 25 minutes or until golden. May sprinkle with more sugar substitute after removing from oven.

Serves 6.

FRUITCAKE

EACH SERVING Amount: 1 slice
Exchanges: 1/8 bread
               3/4 fruit
               3/4 fat

Chol: 12 mg   Carbo: 11 gm Fat: 4 gm
Calories: 80   Protein: 2 gm Fiber: 1 gm
Sodium: 23 mg

INGREDIENTS:
1 C. raisins
1/2 C. chopped dried apricots
1/2 C. chopped pitted dates
1/2 C. chopped walnuts
1 C. whole wheat flour
1/4 C. unsweetened coconut
6 Tbsp. corn oil
1 Tbsp. vanilla extract
1/4 tsp. salt
2 eggs, beaten (may substitute 1/2 C. egg substitute)
1 (16 oz.) can crushed pineapple, in own juice,
   drained (save 3 Tbsp. for glaze)

STEPS IN PREPARATION:
1. Preheat oven to 350 degrees.
2. Combine first 5 ingredients, mixing flour well with dried fruit.Mix remaining ingredients separately and add to first, stirring well.
3. Pour into regular loaf pan that has been sprayed with non-stick spray. Bake 1 hour.
4. Remove from oven, pour on glaze, punching holes all over to penetrate cake.
Serves 36.

Glaze: Mix 3 Tbsp. heated pineapple juice with 6 packages of sugar substitute. Pour over cake.

APPLESAUCE CAKE

EACH SERVING Amount: 1 slice
Exchanges: 3/4 bread
1/2 fruit
1 fat

Chol: 0   Carbo: 20 gm   Fat: 4 gm
Calories: 122 Protein: 2 gm   Fiber: 1 gm
Sodium: 143 mg

INGREDIENTS:

1/2 C. diet margarine
4 tsp. brown sugar substitute
1 C. cold unsweetened applesauce
2 C. all purpose flour
1 tsp. soda
1/4 tsp. salt
1/2 tsp. cinnamon
1/4 tsp. powdered cloves
1 C. raisins
1/4 C. chopped pecans

STEPS IN PREPARATION:

1. Cream margarine; beat in brown sugar substitute gradually. Add applesauce. Add flour sifted with soda, salt and spices. Add raisins and nuts.
2. Spread in a 9" pan that has been sprayed with non-stick spray and floured.
3. Bake 25 minutes at 350 degrees.

Serves 16

QUICK CHEESE CAKE

EACH SERVING Amount: 1 portion
Exchanges: 3/4 bread
2-1/2 fat

Chol: 16 mg   **Carbo:** 12 gm   **Fat:** 14 gm
Calories: 184   **Protein:** 4 gm   **Fiber:** Tr.
Sodium: 237 mg

INGREDIENTS:

Crust:
1 stick diet margarine
1 C. flour
1 Tbsp. chopped pecans

Filling:
8 oz. lite cream cheese, softened
8 oz. plain non-fat yogurt
1 tsp. vanilla
10 pkgs. sugar substitute
1 pkg. sugar-free whipped topping

STEPS IN PREPARATION:

1. Process crust ingredients in food processor or by hand until it will form a ball. Press into 10-inch pie pan.
2. Bake at 350 degrees for 20 minutes. Cool completely.
3. Beat cream cheese until smooth. Add yogurt, vanilla and sugar substitute, blend well. Blend prepared topping into cream cheese mixture.
4. Put into cooled crust and chill thoroughly. Serve with fruit garnish, if desired.

Serves 12
Add appropriate fruit exchanges if fruit is used.

FRUIT JUICE CAKE

Chol: 19 mg **Carbo:** 16 gm **Fat:** 2 gm
Calories: 99 **Protein:** 4 gm **Fiber:** 2 gm
Sodium: 218 mg

INGREDIENTS:

9 finely chopped prunes
1 Tbsp. grated orange peel
1/2 C. non-fat dry powdered milk
4 Tbsp. softened diet margarine
1 egg beaten
3/4 C. orange juice
1 C. flour, whole wheat or unbleached
1 1/2 tsp. baking powder
1/2 tsp. salt

STEPS IN PREPARATION:

1. Combine prunes and orange peel and set aside.
2. Cream dry milk with margarine. Add egg and orange juice and mix well.
3. In another bowl, combine flour, baking powder and salt. Add prune mixture and stir well. Stir dry ingredients into orange juice mixture and mix well.
4. Pour into 9X5X3 pan sprayed with non-stick spray . Bake at 325 degrees for 45 minutes or until appears done. Remove from oven and cool on rack.

Serves 12

APPLESAUCE CUPCAKES

EACH SERVING Amount: 1 cupcake
Exchanges: 3/4 bread
1 fat

Chol: 17 mg   **Carbo:** 14 gm   **Fat:** 4 gm
Calories: 105   **Protein:** 2 gm   **Fiber:** Tr.
Sodium: 178 mg

INGREDIENTS:
6 Tbsp. diet margarine
1 egg
6 pkgs. sugar substitute to equal 1/4 C. sugar
1 1/2 C. sifted flour
1 tsp. baking soda
1/4 tsp. salt
1 tsp. cinnamon
1 1/2 tsp. nutmeg
1 C. unsweetened applesauce
1 tsp. vanilla
8 chopped walnuts

STEPS IN PREPARATION:
1. Preheat oven to 375 degrees.
2. Cream margarine until fluffy.
3. Beat egg and sugar substitute; add to margarine and blend.
4. Sift together dry ingredients. Add to margarine mixture alternately with applesauce, mixing well after each addition. Stir in vanilla and nuts.
5. Spoon into 12 cupcake pans sprayed with non-stick spray. Bake 15 to 20 minutes.
Serves 12

CHOCOLATE ANGEL CAKE

Chol: 0   **Carbo:** 10 gm **Fat:** Tr.
Calories: 52 **Protein:** 4 gm **Fiber:** .3 gm
Sodium: 103 mg

INGREDIENTS:

1 C. cake flour
1 pkg. sugar substitute
3 Tbsp. unsweetened cocoa
10 egg whites
1 1/2 tsp. cream of tartar
1 1/2 tsp. vanilla
1/4 tsp. salt
3 pkgs. sugar substitute

STEPS IN PREPARATION:

1. Preheat oven to 350 degrees.
2. Sift together flour, 1 pkg. sugar substitute, and 3 Tbsp. cocoa into bowl; repeat sifting. Set aside.
3. In a large mixing bowl beat egg whites with cream of tartar, vanilla, and salt at medium speed till soft peaks form. Gradually add 3 pkg. sugar substitute, beating at high speed till stiff peaks form. Fold in remaining ingredients. Bake at 350 degrees for 25 minutes.

Serves 12

CHEWY CHOCOLATE BROWNIES

EACH SERVING Amount: 2 brownies
Exchanges: 1/2 bread
1/2 fat

Chol: 14 mg **Carbo:** 7 gm **Fat:** 4 gm
Calories: 67 **Protein:** 2 gm **Fiber:** Tr.
Sodium: 134 mg

INGREDIENTS:

1 C. flour
1 tsp. baking powder
1/4 tsp. salt
1/2 C. diet margarine, melted
3 Tbsp. Cocoa
Sugar substitute (sweeten to taste)
1 tsp. vanilla
2 eggs
1/4 C. canned evaporated skim milk
5 pecan halves, chopped

STEPS IN PREPARATION:
1. Preheat oven to 350 degrees.
2. In a bowl mix flour, baking powder and salt.
3. Beat eggs.
4. Melt margarine.
5. Add all ingredients to flour mixture. Bake for 20 minutes.
Yields 16

PUMPKIN PUFFS

INGREDIENTS:

1 1/2 C. sifted flour
3 tsp. baking powder
3/4 tsp. salt
Sugar substitute to equal 1/2 C. sugar
1/2 tsp. cinnamon
1/2 tsp. nutmeg
4 tsp. vegetable oil + fruit juice to equal 1/4 C.
1 egg, beaten
1/2 C. pumpkin (canned)
1/2 C. skim milk
1/2 C. raisins

STEPS IN PREPARATION:

1. Sift dry ingredients together. Stir in oil. Add egg, pumpkin, and milk. Stir in raisins.
2. Spray muffin tin with non-stick spray or use paper liner.
3. Pour in batter and bake at 400 degrees for 15 - 20 minutes.

Yields: 9 muffins

MICROWAVE CHERRY CREPES

EACH SERVING Amount: 2 crepes
Exchanges: 3/4 fruit

Chol: 0   **Carbo:** 17 gm   **Fat:** Tr.
Calories: 48   **Protein:** 1 gm   **Fiber:** Tr.
Sodium: 23 mg

INGREDIENTS:
Sugar substitute to equal 3/4 C. sugar
2 Tbsp. cornstarch
2 C. cranberry juice cocktail
16 oz. can pitted tart red cherries, drained
1/2 tsp. grated lemon peel
1/4 tsp. vanilla
red food coloring
1 C. plain low-fat yogurt
1/2 tsp. ground cinnamon
16 crepes

STEPS IN PREPARATION:
1. Sauce - In quart glass bowl, combine 1/4 C. sugar substitute and cornstarch. Add next five ingredients. Cook, uncovered, in microwave till thickened and bubbly, 5-7 minutes, stirring after each minute. Set aside.
2. Filling - Combine yogurt, remaining sugar substitute, and cinnamon.
3. Spread filling mixture over unbrowned side of each crepe, made from your favorite crepe recipe, leaving 1/4-inch rim around edge. Roll up as for jelly roll.
4. Place seam side down in 12X7X2 baking dish, forming two layers.
5. Spoon sauce over crepes. Microwave, covered, about 4 minutes; turn dish once.
Serves 8

PUMPKIN CUSTARD

EACH SERVING Amount: 1/2 cup
Exchanges: 3/4 meat
1/3 bread
1/2 milk

Chol: 72 mg **Carbo:** 12 gm **Fat:** 4 gm
Calories: 124 **Protein:** 9 gm **Fiber:** 1 gm
Sodium: 123 mg

INGREDIENTS:
2 pkgs. unflavored gelatin
1 1/2 C. evaporated skim milk
4 eggs, separated
4 Tbsp. brown sugar substitute
1 1/2 C. canned pumpkin
1/2 tsp. pumpkin pie spice
2 tsp. vanilla

STEPS IN PREPARATION:
1. Sprinkle gelatin over milk; let soften.
2. In a small saucepan, combine egg yolks and 2 Tbsp. brown sugar substitute. Bring mixture to a boil, stirring constantly; remove from heat. Add pumpkin and spice. Cool until slightly thickened.
3. Beat egg whites until stiff peaks form; add remaining tablespoon brown sugar substitute. Add vanilla; fold egg whites into pumpkin mixture.
4. Divide custard among 6 dessert dishes; chill in refrigerator until firm.

Serves 6

OH-SO-CREAMY BANANA PUDDING

EACH SERVING **Amount:** 1 portion
Exchanges: 1 fruit
1 milk
1/2 fat

Chol: 5 mg   **Carbo:** 35 gm **Fat:** 3 gm
Calories: 180 **Protein:** 13 gm **Fiber:** 2 gm
Sodium: 144 mg

INGREDIENTS:
1/4 C. cold water
1 env. unflavored gelatin
Sugar substitute to equal 8 tsp. sugar
1/3 C. non-fat dry powdered milk
1 C. skim milk
1 tsp. vanilla extract
1 tsp. butter flavoring
1/2 C. hot water
1 banana, 9 inch
6 Tbsp. prepared sugar-free whipped topping

STEPS IN PREPARATION:
1. In blender mix cold water, unflavored gelatin and sugar substitute. Add rest of ingredients except banana and blend well. By hand fold in topping.
2. Slice banana and line 1/2 of slices in each 8 oz. serving dish. Pour 1/2 of pudding into each dish over banana slices. Refrigerate 3 to 4 hours.

Serves 2.

FIRST PLACE WHIPPED CREAM

EACH SERVING Amount: 1 Tbsp. = free
Exchanges: 1/4 cup = 1/2 fat

Chol: Tr.   **Carbo:** 2 gm   **Fat:** Tr.
Calories: 39   **Protein:** 1 gm **Fiber:** 0
Sodium: 13 mg

INGREDIENTS:
1 tsp. granulated gelatin
1 Tbsp. cold water
2 1/2 Tbsp. boiling water
1/2 C. iced water
1/2 C. non-fat dry powdered milk
5 pkgs. sugar substitute
1/2 tsp. vanilla
2 Tbsp. vegetable oil

STEPS IN PREPARATION:
1. Chill a small mixing bowl and beaters.
2. Meanwhile, soften gelatin in cold water, then dissolve it over boiling water. Allow it to cool until warm.
3. Place iced water and non-fat dry milk in chilled bowl and beat at high speed until stiff peaks form. Continue beating, adding remaining ingredients and gelatin, until blended.
4. Place bowl in freezer for 15 minutes, then transfer to refrigerator. Occasionally stir gently to keep mixture smooth and well blended. Makes 3 cups or 24 servings.

PINEAPPLE-BANANA PIE

EACH SERVING Amount: 1 slice
Exchanges: 1/4 bread
1/4 fruit
1/3 milk

Chol: Tr.   Carbo: 16 gm Fat: Tr.
Calories: 80   Protein: 4 gm Fiber: 1 gm
Sodium: 84 mg

INGREDIENTS:

1-4 serving package sugar-free vanilla pudding (Not Instant)

1 banana

1 (8 oz.) can crushed unsweetened pineapple

1 C. skim milk

3 pkgs. sugar substitute

1 tsp. vanilla

STEPS IN PREPARATION:

1. Cook pudding mixed with sugar substitute, pineapple juice and milk until it thickens. Remove from heat - add pineapple and 1 tsp. vanilla. Mix well.

2. Slice banana over a cooked pie crust. Pour pudding over banana.

Exchange for pie crust is not included.

Serves 8.

BLACK BOTTOM PIE

EACH SERVING Amount: 1 slice
Exchanges: includes pie crust
1/2 bread
1/2 milk
1 fat

Chol: 8 mg   **Carbo:** 7 gm   **Fat:** 3 gm
Calories: 78   **Protein:** 2 gm   **Fiber:** Tr.
Sodium: 76 mg

INGREDIENTS:
1 env. unflavored gelatin
1 1/2 C. skim milk
3/4 C. part-skim ricotta
1 Tbsp. vanilla extract
6 pkgs. sugar substitute
1/4 C. cocoa powder
1 packet sugar-free whpped topping
6 pkgs. sugar substitute
All-Bran Pie Crust, see page 235

STEPS IN PREPARATION:
1. In small saucepan, sprinkle gelatin over 1/2 cup of skim milk. Let stand 1 minute. Heat, stirring constantly until gelatin dissolves.
2. In blender or food processor, blend ricotta until smooth and add gelatin mixture, rest of milk and vanilla. Continue blending until completely smooth. Remove half of mixture and set aside.
3. To mixture in blender, add 6 packets sugar substitute and cocoa. Blend thoroughly. Pour into crust. Chill 30 minutes or until partially set.

4. At the same time, chill remaining mixture for 30 minutes.
5. Prepare sugar-free whipped topping according o package directions, gradually adding 6 pkg. sugar substitute. Whisk into reserved, chilled mixture until blended smoothly. Spoon over chocolate layer; chill until set.
6. Garnish with dusting of cocoa.

Crust: All-Bran Pie Crust Mix - Exchanges for pie crust are included.

Serves 8

BLUEBERRY CREAM PIE

EACH SERVING Amount: 1 slice
Exchanges: 1 bread
                   3/4 fruit
                   1/2 milk
                   1/2 fat

Chol: 1 mg   **Carbo:** 19 gm   **Fat:** 1 gm
Calories: 96   **Protein:** 3 gm **Fiber:** 3 gm
Sodium: 71 mg

INGREDIENTS:
Filling:
4 C. fresh/frozen blueberries
2 Tbsp. flour
1 Tbsp. lemon juice
1/8 tsp. nutmeg
sugar substitute to taste
1 small pkg. sugar-free instant pudding
1 pkg. sugar-free whipped topping

STEPS IN PREPARATION:
1. Combine half of the berries and all ingredients except sugar substitute in saucepan and bring to boil. Reduce heat, cover tightly, and simmer for about 10-15 minutes. Remove from heat, cool slightly, add remaining berries and sugar substitute to taste, and cool completely. Pour into cooled crust.
2. Mix 1 small pkg. sugar-free instant vanilla pudding according to directions on package. Pour over refrigerated pie. Prepare 1 pkg. sugar-free whipped topping mixed according to directions on package for final topping and garnish with a few blueberries saved back.

Crust: All-Bran Pie Crust Mix - Exchanges for pie crust are included. See page 235.
Serves 8

BANANA CREAM PIE

EACH SERVING **Amount:** 1 slice
Exchanges: includes pie crust
1-1/2 bread
1 fruit
3/4 milk
1/2 fat

Chol: 1 mg   **Carbo:** 17 gm **Fat:** Tr.
Calories: 82   **Protein:** 3 gm **Fiber:** 1 gm
Sodium: 88 mg

INGREDIENTS:

1 pie crust - All-Bran Crust, see page 235
1 small pkg. vanilla sugar-free instant pudding
3 small bananas
Low-calorie whipped topping

STEPS IN PREPARATION:

1. Mix pudding according to package directions.
2. Layer bananas and pudding twice in crust.
   Dab low-calorie whipped topping on top. Chill.

Exchange for pie crust is included.
Serves 6.

EASY PUMPKIN PIE

EACH SERVING Amount: 1 slice
Exchanges: 1/2 bread
              1/4 milk

Chol: 28 mg   Carbo: 16 gm Fat: 2 gm
Calories: 107 Protein: 6 gm Fiber: 2 gm
Sodium: 169 mg

INGREDIENTS:

1 (16-oz.) can solid packed pumpkin
1 (13-oz.) can evaporated skim milk
1 egg
2 egg whites
1/2 C. Buttermilk Biscuit Mix
8 pkgs. sugar substitute
2 tsp. pumpkin pie spice
2 tsp. vanilla

STEPS IN PREPARATION:

1. Place all ingredients in blender and process till smooth. Pour into pie pan.
2. Bake at 350 degrees for 50 minutes or until center is puffed up.

Serves 8.

PUMPKIN PIE

EACH SERVING Amount: 1 slice
Exchanges: 1/4 meat
1 bread
1/2 milk
1 fat

Chol: 54 mg   **Carbo:** 30 gm **Fat:** 6 gm
Calories: 185 **Protein:** 6 gm **Fiber:** 1 gm
Sodium: 271 mg

INGREDIENTS:
1- 9 inch pie shell
1 1/4 C. cooked pumpkin
sugar substitute to equal 1/2 C. sugar
1/2 tsp. salt
1/2 tsp. ginger
1 tsp. cinnamon
1/4 tsp. nutmeg
1/4 tsp. cloves
2 slightly beaten eggs
1 1/2 C. canned evaporated skim milk

STEPS IN PREPARATION
1. Combine pumpkin, sugar substitute, and spices until well blended. Stir in slightly beaten eggs until mixed thoroughly. Gradually add skim milk and blend well.
2. Pour into pie shell and bake in 400 degree oven for about 40 minutes, or until knife inserted between center and the edge comes out clean.

Serves 8.

FRESH STRAWBERRY PIE

EACH SERVING Amount: 1 slice
Exchanges: 3/4 bread
1/2 fruit
1 fat

Chol: 0   Carbo: 8 gm   Fat: 1 gm
Calories: 49   Protein: 1 gm Fiber: 1 gm
Sodium: 26 mg

INGREDIENTS:

3 pkgs. sugar substitute
1 small box sugar-free strawberry gelatin
3 C. fresh or frozen strawberries
3 Tbsp. cornstarch
1 C. hot water
1 baked pie crust - All-Bran Crust, see page 235
1 pkg. prepared low-calorie whipped topping

STEPS IN PREPARATION:

1. Mix gelatin, cornstarch, and hot water and cook about 1 minute. Add sugar substitute and cool. Add sliced strawberries to gelatin mixture and coat.
2. Pour into cooled 9" pie shell and refrigerate. Top with low-calorie whipped topping before serving.

Serves 8

FUDGE PIE

EACH SERVING Amount: 1 slice
Exchanges: 1/4 meat
                    1 1/2 bread
                    1/4 milk
                    1 fat

Chol: 54 mg   **Carbo:** 11 gm **Fat:** 4 gm
Calories: 100 **Protein:** 4 gm **Fiber:** Tr.
Sodium: 100 mg

INGREDIENTS:

4 Tbsp. diet margarine
2 Tbsp. Cocoa
1/2 C. canned evaporated skim milk
2 eggs
10 pkgs. sugar substitute
1 tsp. vanilla
1/2 C. flour
Chocolate Sauce see page 229

STEPS IN PREPARATION:

1. Combine margarine, cocoa, and milk in small sauce pan; cook over low heat until melted. Set aside.
2. Combine eggs, artifical sweetener, & vanilla in medium bowl, stirring well. Stir in chocolate mixture. Add flour; stir until blended.
3. Pour mixture into 9" pie pan.
4. Bake 325 degrees for 25 minutes.
Serves 8.

CHOCOLATE SAUCE

Chol: 1 mg   Carbo: 5 gm   Fat: Tr.
Calories: 27   Protein: 2 gm   Fiber: Tr.
Sodium: 35 mg

INGREDIENTS:

1 Tbsp. plus 1 tsp. cocoa
2 Tbsp. water
2 tsp. cornstarch
1/2 tsp. powder butter flavoring
3/4 C. evaporated skim milk
5 pkgs. sugar substitute

STEPS IN PREPARATION:

1. In small sauce pan, combine cocoa, water, cornstarch, and powder butter flavoring; stir until well mixed. Add milk; cook, stirring constantly until mixture comes to a boil. Remove from heat; add sugar substitute.
2. Cover & chill.
Serves 8.

THREE LAYER APPLE/RAISIN PIE

EACH SERVING Amount: 1 slice
Exchanges: 1 1/4 bread
                1 fruit
                1/2 milk
                1 1/2 fat

Chol: 2 mg   **Carbo:** 33 gm   **Fat:** .5 gm
Calories: 159   **Protein:** 5 gm   **Fiber:** 2 gm
Sodium: 134 mg

INGREDIENTS:

1 pkg. dried apples
1/2 C. raisins
1 tsp. cinnamon
1 Tbsp. cornstarch
1 large package sugar-free vanilla pudding
1 pkg. sugar-free whipped topping prepared with
    1/2 C. milk instead of water
4 packets sugar substitute (add to cooked,
    cooled apples)

STEPS IN PREPARATION:

1. Add three cups water to the dried apples,
   soak a few minutes if time permits.
2. Cook at low heat for 30 minutes. Add raisins
   and cinnamon and cook another 15 minutes.
3. Dissolve cornstarch with a small amount of
   water and add to boiling apples. Cook 5
   minutes and set aside to cool. After apples
   have cooled, add to a cooked, cooled pie
   crust.
4. Mix pudding according to directions. Pour
   pudding over the apple filling and place in the

refrigerator while preparing the low calorie whipped topping. Add the topping and refrigerate.

Exchange includes the Easy No-Roll Pie Crust. See page 236.

Serves 8

CHOCOLATE PIE

EACH SERVING Amount: 1 slice
Exchanges: 1/3 meat
2 fat

Chol: 11 mg   **Carbo:** 8 gm   **Fat:** 7 gm
Calories: 107   **Protein:** 3 gm   **Fiber:** Tr.
Sodium: 75 mg

INGREDIENTS:

3 oz. lite cream cheese
9 pkgs. sugar substitute
1 tsp. vanilla
8 oz. (2 1/2 C.) sugar-free whipped topping
1/3 C. skim milk
1/3 C. cocoa

STEPS IN PREPARATION:

1. In mixer cream together cheese, sugar substitute and vanilla. Add alternately milk and cocoa. Beat until smooth.
2. Gradually fold in whipped topping and put in pie shell and chill or freeze.

Add correct count for crust of your choice.

BLUEBERRY PIE

EACH SERVING Amount: 1 slice
Exchanges: 1 meat
1/4 fruit
1/2 milk

Chol: 122 mg **Carbo:** 25 gm **Fat:** 3 gm
Calories: 155 **Protein:** 9 gm **Fiber:** 1 gm
Sodium: 322 mg

INGREDIENTS:
Filling: 1 pkg. unflavored gelatin
8 oz. diet cream soda
8 oz. evaporated skim milk
2 eggs
3/4 tsp. vanilla extract
2 Tbsp. brown sugar substitute
Mock Sour Cream:
2/3 C. ricotta cheese, low-fat
1/4 tsp. salt
1 tsp. lemon juice
2 oz. buttermilk, low-fat
2 tsp. brown sugar substitute
Topping: 1/2 tsp. unflavored gelatin
1/4 C. cold water
1 C. frozen unsweetened blueberries
1 pkg. sugar substitute

STEPS IN PREPARATION:
1. Soften gelatin in soda. Heat, stirring constantly until gelatin dissolves. Add milk.
2. In small bowl, beat eggs thoroughly and add to first mixture, stirring constantly over low heat until mixture thickens. Remove from

heat and add vanilla and brown sugar substitute. Mix and pour into 10-inch pie pan. Refrigerate until set.

3. In blender combine all ingredients for Mock Sour Cream and blend until smooth and shiny. Pour over chilled pie filling.

4. To make topping, soften gelatin in water. Add blueberries. Simmer 4 minutes. Remove from heat and stir in sweetener. Refrigerate until thick. Use this to make border on top of pie.

Serves 4

ALL-BRAN PIE CRUST

EACH SERVING Amount: 1 slice
Exchanges: 1 bread
              1/4 fat

Chol: 0   **Carbo:** 9 gm   **Fat:** 2 gm
Calories: 63   **Protein:** 2 gm   **Fiber:** 7 gm
Sodium: 163 mg

INGREDIENTS:
1 C. All-Bran cereal

4 T. flour

2 T. diet margarine, melted

1/2 C. apple juice

STEPS IN PREPARATION:
1. Combine all ingredients. Press into pan sprayed with non-stick cooking spray.
2. Bake at 375 degrees 12 minutes. Allow to cool.

Serves 8

EASY NO-ROLL PIE CRUST

EACH SERVING Amount: 1 slice
Exchanges: 1/2 bread
1 fat

Chol: Tr.   Carbo: 11 gm   Fat: 5 gm
Calories: 95   Protein: 2 gm   Fiber: Tr.
Sodium: 76 mg

INGREDIENTS:

1 C. flour
8 tsp. vegetable oil
1/4 C. 1/2% milk + 1 tsp.
1/4 tsp. salt

STEPS IN PREPARATION:

1. Mix all ingredients in a bowl. Stir with a fork.
2. Place in a pie plate and press pie crust out with fingers.
3. Bake at 400 degrees for 5 minutes or until brown.

Serves 8.

OLD FASHIONED PIE CRUST

EACH SERVING Amount: 1 slice
Exchanges: 1/2 bread
1/4 fat

Chol: 0   **Carbo:** 5 gm   **Fat:** 2 gm
Calories: 41   **Protein:** 1 gm   **Fiber:** Tr.
Sodium: 175 mg

INGREDIENTS:

1/2 C. flour
1/2 tsp. salt
2 Tbsp. + 1 tsp. diet margarine
1 to 2 Tbsp. cold water

STEPS IN PREPARATION:

1. Combine flour and salt. Cut in margarine until mixture looks like cornmeal. Add water gradually until dough is moistened and just holds together.
2. Roll between sheets of waxed paper, or use a lightly floured pastry cloth. Roll thin, press into pie pan, prick with fork.
3. Bake in 425 degrees for 15 minutes.
Serves 8.

APPLE PAN DOWDY

EACH SERVING Amount: 1 portion
Exchanges: 1/2 bread
1/2 fruit
1/2 fat

Chol: 18 mg   **Carbo:** 21 gm   **Fat:** 2 gm
Calories: 110   **Protein:** 2 gm   **Fiber:** Tr.
Sodium: 206 mg

INGREDIENTS:
3 Tbsp. diet margarine
2 tsp. brown sugar substitute
1 egg
1 1/2 C. flour
2 tsp. baking powder
1/4 tsp. salt
1/2 C. low-fat milk
6 sliced apples
1 tsp. brown sugar substitute
1/4 tsp. nutmeg
1/4 tsp. salt

STEPS IN PREPARATION:
Batter:
1. Cream margarine. Gradually add brown sugar substitute; add egg.
2. Mix then sift flour, baking powder, and salt. Add alternately with milk to first mixture.

Filling:
1. Put apples in lightly buttered baking dish, sprayed with non stick cooking spray. Mix brown sugar substitute, nutmeg, and salt. Sprinkle over apples.

2. Bake at 350 degrees until apples are soft. Pour batter over the apples and continue baking for 40 minutes.
Serves 12.

FRENCH APPLE TART

EACH SERVING Amount: 1 slice
Exchanges: 1 bread
1 fruit

Chol: 0 Carbo: 33 gm Fat: Tr.
Calories: 143 Protein: 2 gm Fiber: 3 gm
Sodium: 129 mg

INGREDIENTS:

1 C. + 2 Tbsp. Grape Nuts cereal
3 Tbsp. apple juice concentrate
1/2 tsp. cinnamon
3 medium apples, peeled, cored and thinly sliced
2 tsp. lemon juice
1 Tbsp. cornstarch
1/3 C. apple juice concentrate
2/3 C. water

STEPS IN PREPARATION:

1. Moisten the cereal with 3 Tbsp. apple juice concentrate in a 9 X 9 inch non-stick baking pan and pat into a thin layer. Sprinkle with 1/4 tsp. of the cinnamon.
2. Arrange the sliced apples in rows overlapping slightly. If you're using a round baking pan, arrange the sliced apples in concentric circles. Sprinkle with lemon juice and 1/4 tsp. of the cinnamon.Cover with aluminum foil.
3. Bake in a 350 degree oven for 45 minutes or until apples are tender. Remove tart from oven and cool to room temperature.
4. Combine cornstarch, 1/3 cup apple juice concentrate and water in a saucepan. Cook

and stir over medium heat until mixture thickens and is clear.

5. Spoon the cornstarch, apple juice concentrate, and water mixture over the tart or glaze with a pastry brush. You may either chill the tart to be served later or leave at room temperature to serve.

Serves 6.

APPLE STRUDEL

EACH SERVING Amount: 1 slice
Exchanges: 1 bread
1/2 fruit
1/2 fat

Chol: 0   Carbo: 21 gm   Fat: 7 gm
Calories: 152   Protein: 2 gm   Fiber: 1 gm
Sodium: 212 mg

INGREDIENTS:
1 C. applesauce (no sugar added)
1 apple, peeled, cored and sliced
2 Tbsp. raisins
2 pkgs. sugar substitute
cinnamon and nutmeg to taste
1 (10 count) can low-fat biscuits
8 tsp. diet margarine

STEPS IN PREPARATION:
1. Spray cookie sheet with non-stick spray and open dough onto sheet, pressing out to make crust.
2. Spread apple mix evenly onto dough and roll up like a jelly roll. Spread 8 tsp. diet margarine on top and bake 5 minutes. Let cool.

Serves 8

LUSCIOUS LEMON FROTH

EACH SERVING Amount: 1 portion
Exchanges: 3/4 milk

Chol: 2 mg   **Carbo:** 10 gm   **Fat:** Tr.
Calories: 81   **Protein:** 8 gm   **Fiber:** 0
Sodium: 164 mg

INGREDIENTS:
1/2 C. non-fat plain yogurt
1/3 small box sugar-free gelatin, lemon
1 C. skim milk
1 to 2 pkgs. of sugar substitute (optional)
3 or 4 ice cubes crushed
1/2 of a 12 oz. can of a diet lemon-lime drink

STEPS IN PREPARATION:
1. Blend everything but the soda well in shaker, blender or processor until frothy.
2. Add soda, blend a few seconds more until even frothier, then pour into 2 tall glasses.

Serves 2

ORANGE-PINEAPPLE ICE CREAM

EACH SERVING Amount: 1 portion
Exchanges: 1 fruit
              1/2 milk

Chol: 1 mg   Carbo: 14 gm   Fat: Tr.
Calories: 72   Protein: 4 gm Fiber: Tr.
Sodium: 57 mg

INGREDIENTS:

1 can evaporated skim milk, chilled
1 (6 oz.) can undiluted frozen orange juice
  concentrate
8 slices pineapple, canned in own juice
2 pkgs. sugar substitute

STEPS IN PREPARATION:

1. Beat ice cold milk until stiff like whipped cream.
   Stir in orange juice concentrate, pineapple,
   and sugar substitute and mix well.
2. Pour into 10 equal covered containers (or 1
   large container to be divided into eighths after
   freezing). Freeze until hard.
Serves 8

QUICK PARFAIT

EACH SERVING Amount: 2 portions
Exchanges: 1/4 fat

Chol: 0   **Carbo:** 1 gm   **Fat:** 2 gm
Calories: 23   **Protein:** 1 gm **Fiber:** 0
Sodium: 33 mg

INGREDIENTS:
3/4 C. boiling water
1 small pkg. sugar-free gelatin, any flavor
1/2 C. cold water
Ice cubes
1/2 C. sugar-free whipped topping

STEPS IN PREPARATION:
1. Pour boiling water into blender container. Add gelatin and blend at low speed until dissolved, about 30 seconds.
2. Combine cold water and ice cubes to make 1 1/4 cups. Add to gelatin and stir until ice is partially melted, then blend at high speed for 10 seconds. Add whipped topping and blend 15 seconds.
3. Pour half the mixture into 6 straight-sided dessert glasses, then fill glasses with remaining mixture. Chill until set, about 1 hour.

Serves 6

VARIATION: FRESH FRUIT PARFAIT
Place 1/4 C. sliced strawberries, peaches or melon balls in the bottom of each glass. Then add gelatin mixture. Add 1/4 fruit to exchanges.

APPLESAUCE YOGURT DESSERT

EACH SERVING Amount: 1 portion
Exchanges: 1/4 fruit
                 1/8 milk

Chol: 0   **Carbo:** 7 gm   **Fat:** Tr.
Calories: 39   **Protein:** 2 gm   **Fiber:** Tr.
Sodium: 73 mg

INGREDIENTS:

1 sm. pkg. sugar-free gelatin, raspberry
1 C. boiling water
3/4 C. chilled, unsweetened applesauce
1/4 tsp. cinnamon
1/2 C. plain low-fat yogurt
1 tsp. vanilla

STEPS IN PREPARATION:

1. Dissolve gelatin in boiling water. Measure 3/4 cup; add applesauce and cinnamon. Pour into 4 dessert glasses and chill until set but not firm.
2. Chill remaining gelatin until slightly thickened, then blend in yogurt and spoon over gelatin in glasses. Garnish with additional yogurt, if desired.

Serves 4

ICE CREAM

EACH SERVING Amount: 1 portion
Exchanges: 1/2 meat
1 fruit
1 milk
1 fat

Chol: 112 mg **Carbo:** 31 gm **Fat:** 3 gm
Calories: 224 **Protein:** 16 gm **Fiber:** 2 gm
Sodium: 237 mg

INGREDIENTS:

4 eggs - beat until foamy; gradually add 16 pkgs.
of sugar substitute
2 (12 oz.) cans evaporated skim milk
1 Tbsp. vanilla
6 oz. bananas - mashed
4 C. strawberries, or 2 C. peaches and
2 C. strawberries
juice of 1 lemon
2 C. of 1/2% milk

STEPS IN PREPARATION:

1. Mix all ingredients in bowl.
2. Pour into ice cream maker and freeze according to manufacturer's directions.

Serves 8.

FROZEN BLUEBERRY YOGURT

EACH SERVING **Amount:** 1 cup
Exchanges: 1/2 fruit
1/4 milk

Chol: 0   **Carbo:** 17 gm   **Fat:** Tr.
Calories: 82   **Protein:** 4 gm   **Fiber:** 2 gm
Sodium: 67 mg

INGREDIENTS:

1 small pkg. sugar-free lemon gelatin
1 C. boiling water
5 ice cubes
2 C. non-fat sugar-free vanilla or blueberry yogurt
2 C. fresh or frozen (without sugar) blueberries, crushed or processed
4 pkgs. sugar substitute

STEPS IN PREPARATION:

1. In a large bowl add boiling water to gelatin, mixing until well dissolved. Add ice cubes and stir until melted.
2. With rotary mixer beat gelatin mixture until very light and fluffy. Add the rest of the ingredients and beat until well mixed.
3. Pour into ice cream freezer and freeze according to manufacturer's directions.

Yields 1/2 gallon or 8 one-cup servings.

To make Frozen Strawberry Yogurt:
Use strawberry sugar-free gelatin, 3 cups crushed strawberries, and strawberry syrup. Counts as above.

To make Pina Colada Frozen Gelatin Yogurt:
Use Hawaiian Pineapple sugar-free gelatin, 2 mashed ripe bananas, 1/2 tsp. strawberry extract, and 1/2 tsp. coconut extract.

To double the above recipe, still only use one small package of sugar-free gelatin.

BANANA CAKE

EACH SERVING **Amount:** 1 slice
Exchanges: 1 bread
1/2 fruit
1/2 fat

Chol: 35 mg **Carbo:** 22 gm **Fat:** 3 gm
Calories: 150 **Protein:** 4 gm **Fiber:** 1 gm
Sodium: 178 mg

INGREDIENTS:

1/2 C. diet margarine
6 tsp. brown sugar substitute
2 eggs, slightly beaten
6-3oz. bananas, mashed
2 C. flour
1/2 tsp. baking soda
1/4 tsp. salt
1 C. low-fat milk
1 tsp. vanilla or lemon extract or both

STEPS IN PREPARATION:

1. Cream margarine; add brown sugar substitute gradually. Add eggs and beat thoroughly. Add mashed bananas and flavoring.
2. Sift dry ingredients together and add alternately with milk.
3. Bake at 350 degrees in a 8 to 9 inch cake pan for 20 to 30 minutes.

Serves 12.

BREAKFAST

SUNRISE SHAKE

EACH SERVING Amount: 1 serving
Exchanges: 1 meat
1 1/2 fruit
1/2 milk
1/2 fat

Chol: 216 mg **Carbo:** 52 gm **Fat:** 3 gm
Calories: 317 **Protein:** 16 gm **Fiber:** 3 gm
Sodium: 185 mg

INGREDIENTS:

1/2 C. orange juice
1 1/2 oz. banana
1/4 C. non-fat vanilla yogurt
1 egg
2 Tbsp. non-fat dry powdered milk

STEPS IN PREPARATION:

Put all ingredients in blender jar. Cover. Blend
until smooth.
Serves 1

MILK SHAKE FOR BREAKFAST

EACH SERVING Amount: 1 serving
Exchanges: 1 meat
1 1/2 milk

Chol: 222 mg **Carbo:** 27 gm **Fat:** 5 gm
Calories: 268 **Protein:** 24 gm **Fiber:** 0
Sodium: 344 mg

INGREDIENTS:
1/3 C. non-fat dry powdered milk
1 Tbsp. cocoa
1 medium egg
1/2 C. evaporated skimmed milk
*5-7 ice cubes (depending on how thick you want it)
1 tsp. vanilla
2-4 pkgs. sugar substitute (sweeten to taste)

STEPS IN PREPARATION:
Mix all ingredients in blender for 1 minute.
Serves 1

*If possible, crush ice cubes before putting in blender.

Supplement with one bread serving, and you will make one complete breakfast meal.

BANANA FRENCH TOAST

EACH SERVING Amount: 2 slices
Exchanges: 1 fruit
1 bread

Chol: 1 mg   **Carbo:** 23 gm **Fat:** 1 gm
Calories: 120 **Protein:** 7 gm **Fiber:** 4 gm
Sodium: 169 mg

INGREDIENTS:
1 banana (6 oz.), thickly sliced
1/4 C. skim milk
1 tsp. vanilla extract
1 tsp. ground cinnamon
1 egg white
4 slices lite whole wheat bread

STEPS IN PREPARATION:
1. Preheat oven to 350 degrees.
2. Place all ingredients except bread in a blender and puree. Pour mixture into a shallow bowl.
3. Dip both sides of each slice of bread in the mixture, and place bread on a non-stick baking sheet or a regular baking sheet coated with a non-stick cooking spray.
4. Bake 15 minutes. Serve immediately.
Serves 2

KAISERSCHMARREN (Raisin Pancake)

EACH SERVING Amount: 1 portion
Exchanges: 1 bread
1 fruit
1/2 fat

Chol: 36 mg   **Carbo:** 32 gm   **Fat:** 4 gm
Calories: 178   **Protein:** 5 gm   **Fiber:** 2 gm
Sodium: 281 mg

INGREDIENTS:
3/4 C. raisins
2 Tbsp. orange juice, unsweetened
1 egg, separated
1 C. 1/2% milk
2 pkg. sugar substitute
1/2 tsp. salt
1 C. flour
3 Tbsp. diet margarine
sliced strawberries

STEPS IN PREPARATION:
1. In small bowl, toss raisins with orange juice; set aside 1 hour.
2. In large bowl, whisk together egg yolk and milk. Gradually whisk in 1 pkg. of the sugar substitute, the salt and flour to make a smooth batter.
3. In small bowl, beat egg whites until soft peaks form. Fold egg whites into yolk mixture until white streaks disappear. In 12-inch heavy skillet, heat 2 Tbsp. margarine to bubbling over low heat. Tilt skillet to cover with margarine. Pour in batter and sprinkle evenly with raisin mixture. Cook until browned on one side and almost set, about 10 minutes.
4. Cut pancake into quarters. With broad spatula,

turn pieces over and continue to cook 5 to 8 minutes or until browned and cooked through.
5. With 2 forks, tear into pieces about 2 inches square. Dot with remaining margarine and sprinkle with remaining sugar substitute. Gently toss over low heat until lightly glazed, about 5 minutes. Serve hot, topped with berries.

Serves 6

FRESH LEMON MUFFINS

EACH SERVING **Amount:** 2 muffins
Exchanges: 1/2 bread
3/4 fat

Chol: 0   **Carbo:** 8 gm   **Fat:** 4 gm
Calories: 72   **Protein:** 2 gm   **Fiber:** 0
Sodium: 143 mg

INGREDIENTS:
1/2 C. diet margarine
5 pkg.. sugar substitute
2 egg whites
1 Tbsp. grated lemon rind
3 Tbsp. lemon juice
1 C. flour
1 tsp. baking powder
1/8 tsp. salt
2 pkg. sugar substitute
1/4 tsp. ground cinnamon

STEPS IN PREPARATION:
1. Cream margarine; gradually add sugar substitute, beating until light and fluffy. Add egg whites, one at a time, beating well after each addition. Stir in lemon rind and juice.
2. Combine flour, baking powder, and salt; add to creamed mixture, mixing well. Spoon batter into miniature muffin pans srayed with non-stick cooking spray, filling two-thirds full.
3. Combine sugar substitute and cinnamon; sprinkle over each muffin.
4. Bake at 350 degrees for 20 minutes.

Yields 12
Serves 6

APPLE-BRAN MUFFINS

EACH SERVING Amount: 3 muffins
Exchanges: 1/2 meat
               1 bread
               1 fruit
               3/4 milk

Chol: 38 mg   Carbo: 12 gm   Fat: 1 gm
Calories: 77   Protein: 6 gm   Fiber: 1 gm
Sodium: 147 mg

INGREDIENTS:

3 slices stale hi-fiber or whole wheat bread - diced
1 C. non-fat dry powdered milk
1/2 tsp. baking powder
1/2 tsp. baking soda
1 tsp. apple pie spice
1 C. unsweetened apple sauce
2 eggs
4 Tbsp. unprocessed bran
4 Tbsp. raisins

STEPS IN PREPARATION:

1. Combine bread, dry milk, baking powder, baking soda, and apple pie spice in blender. Blend until bread is crumbled. Add apple sauce, eggs, and bran. Blend thoroughly. Stir in raisins. Spoon batter into non-stick muffin cups sprayed with non-stick cooking spray.
2. Bake for 25 minutes in preheated 375 degree oven until golden brown.

Yields 12
Serves 4

BRAN NUT MUFFINS

EACH SERVING Amount: 1 muffin
Exchanges: 1/2 bread
1/2 fruit
1/2 fat (omit fat if no nuts
are used)

Chol: 9 mg   **Carbo:** 17 gm   **Fat:** 2 gm
Calories: 97   **Protein:** 3 gm   **Fiber:** 4 gm
Sodium: 106 mg

INGREDIENTS:
1 1/2 C. All-Bran cereal

1 C. skim milk

2 C. whole wheat flour

2 Tbsp. ground cinnamon

1 tsp. each: baking powder, baking soda

1 egg

1 (20 oz.) can crushed pineapple, in juice

6 oz. ripe banana, mashed

1/2 C. raisins

Optional: 1/2 C. chopped walnuts

STEPS IN PREPARATION:
1. Mix cereal into milk; let stand five minutes.
2. Meanwhile, mix flour, cinnamon, baking powder and baking soda; set aside.
3. Mix egg with undrained pineapple and mashed banana. Thoroughly combine all three mixtures and stir in raisins and walnuts, if you are using them. Spoon batter into 24 non-stick muffin cups that have been sprayed with non-stick cooking spray.
4. Bake in a preheated 375 degree oven for 30 minutes.

Yields 24

DOUBLE APPLE MUFFINS

EACH SERVING Amount: 1 muffin
Exchanges: 1/3 bread
                   1/3 fruit

Chol: 24 mg   **Carbo:** 12 gm   **Fat:** 1 gm
Calories: 60   **Protein:** 2 gm **Fiber:** 1 gm
Sodium: 78 mg

INGREDIENTS:

1 C. whole wheat flour
1/3 C. uncooked whole wheat hot cereal
2 pkg. sugar substitute
1 tsp. each: baking powder, baking soda, apple pie
   spice (or 1/2 tsp. ground cinnamon and 1/4 tsp.
   each: ground nutmeg and allspice, plus a dash of
   ground cloves)
2 eggs, or equivalent egg substitute
1 C. unsweetened applesauce
1/4 tsp. almond flavoring
1/2 C. raisins
1 green apple pared, cored, and minced

STEPS IN PREPARATION:

1. Stir together flour, cereal, sugar substitute, baking
    powder, baking soda and spices; set aside.
2. Beat eggs with applesauce and almond flavoring.
    Thoroughly combine dry and wet mixtures. Stir in
    raisins and minced apple. Divide among 18 non-
    stick muffin cups, sprayed with non-stick cooking
    spray.
3. Bake in a preheated 350 degree oven 25 minutes.
    Leave in pan 2 minutes, then transfer to rack to
    cool.
Yields 18

FRUIT MUFFINS

INGREDIENTS:
  3 large eggs
  1/2 C. diet margarine
  1 (20 oz.) can unsweetened crushed pineapple
  1 (6 oz.) pineapple juice, unsweetened
  2 1/2 C. wheat flour
  1 tsp. baking soda
  2 tsp. baking powder
  1 tsp. cinnamon
  1/4 C. unsweetened coconut
  1/2 C. raisins
  3 pkg. sugar substitute

STEPS IN PREPARATION:
  1. Beat eggs, softened margarine, and pineapple juice together. Mix together flour, baking soda, baking powder, and cinnamon, and add this mixture to dry ingredients. Beat well, then add pineapple, coconut, raisins, and sugar substitute.
  2. Bake at 350 degrees for 20 to 25 minutes.
  Yields 24

APPLESAUCE RAISIN MUFFINS

EACH SERVING Amount: 1 muffin
Exchanges: 1 bread
1/2 fruit

Chol: 18 mg   **Carbo:** 26 gm   **Fat:** 1 gm
Calories: 119   **Protein:** 3 gm   **Fiber:** 1 gm
Sodium: 130 mg

INGREDIENTS:
1 large egg
1/4 C. fruit juice
1 1/3 C. unsweetened applesauce
2 C. flour
3/4 tsp. baking soda
2 tsp. baking powder
1/2 tsp. nutmeg
3/4 tsp. cinnamon
3/4 C. raisins

STEPS IN PREPARATION:
1. Beat together egg, fruit juice, and applesauce. Add flour, baking soda, baking powder, and spices; beat well. Stir in raisins. Spoon batter into muffin tin that has been sprayed with non-stick cooking spray or use paper baking cups.
2. Bake at 375 degrees for 20 to 25 minutes or until firm to the touch and browned. Cool on wire rack. Delicious with lite cream cheese spread on muffins.
Yields 12

APPLESAUCE MUFFINS

EACH SERVING Amount: 3 muffins
Exchanges: 1 bread
1/2 fruit
1 milk

Chol: 20 mg **Carbo:** 14 gm **Fat:** 0
Calories: 87 **Protein:** 6 gm **Fiber:** Tr.
Sodium: 116 mg

INGREDIENTS:
4 oz. uncooked oatmeal
1 1/3 C. non-fat dry powdered milk
1 Tbsp. cinnamon
2 tsp. vanilla
6 pkg. sugar substitute
1 1/3 C. unsweetened applesauce
1 tsp. baking powder
1/2 C. plus 2 Tbsp. sugar-free lemon-lime soda
1 egg

STEPS IN PREPARATION:
1. Mix all ingredients well and pour into muffin tins sprayed with non-stick cooking spray.
2. Bake at 350 degrees for 15 minutes.
Yields 12

PEANUT BUTTER MUFFINS

INGREDIENTS:
4 Tbsp. wheat flour
2 pkg. sugar substitute
1/4 C. skim milk
1/2 tsp. vanilla
1 egg, beaten
3 Tbsp. extra crunchy peanut butter

ICING
1 oz. lite cream cheese
1 tsp. cocoa
3 pkgs. sugar substitute

STEPS IN PREPARATION:
1. Mix first 6 ingredients. Pour into muffin pan.
2. Bake at 400 degrees for 13-15 minutes.
3. Mix icing ingredients together and spread on muffins.

Yields 4

CARROT-RAISIN MUFFINS

EACH SERVING Amount: 1 muffin
Exchanges: 1/2 bread
               1/2 fruit

Chol: 9 mg   **Carbo:** 16 gm **Fat:** 1 gm
Calories: 77 **Protein:** 2 gm **Fiber:** 2 gm
Sodium: 80 mg

INGREDIENTS:
   1/2 C. bran
   1/2 C. wheat flour
   1 tsp. baking powder
   1/4 tsp. cinnamon
   1/8 tsp. nutmeg
   6 pkg. sugar substitute
   1/2 tsp. baking soda
   1/2 C. butter flavoring made into liquid (We used
       Butter Buds. To make into liquid, follow
       instructions on box.)
   1 egg, beaten
   1 C. grated carrots
   1 C. currants (or raisins)

STEPS IN PREPARATION:
   1. Preheat oven to 350 degrees.
   2. Spray the small muffin tins with non-stick
      cooking spray.
   3. In medium bowl, combine bran, flour, baking
      powder, cinnamon, nutmeg, and sugar substitute.
   4. In separate bowl, dissolve baking soda in
      butter flavoring; add thoroughly to dry
      ingredients. Pour into tins.
   5. Bake 15-18 minutes or until toothpick inserted
      into center comes out clean. Cool.
Yields 12

ORANGE BRAN MUFFINS

EACH SERVING Amount: 1 muffin
Exchanges: 1 bread
              1/2 fat

Chol: 19 mg   Carbo: 17 gm   Fat: 3 gm
Calories: 98   Protein: 4 gm   Fiber: 3 gm
Sodium: 103 mg

INGREDIENTS:
1 C. whole wheat flour
3/4 C. Miller's Bran (unprocessed, uncooked wheat bran)
3/4 tsp. soda
1/8 tsp. salt
1 Tbsp. grated orange rind
1 egg
1 Tbsp. vegetable oil
2 Tbsp. brown sugar substitute
1 C. low-fat buttermilk
1/2 C. raisins (optional)

STEPS IN PREPARATION:
1. Preheat oven to 350 degrees.
2. Spray muffin pan with non-stick cooking spray.
3. Combine whole wheat flour, bran, soda, salt, and orange rind. In separate bowl, beat egg and whip in oil, sugar substitute, and low-fat buttermilk.
4. Add dry ingredients to liquid mixture and stir until just blended. Fold in raisins. Spoon mixture into 12 muffin cups.
5. Bake for 25 minutes.
Yields 12

SNACKS

CHOCOLATE "TOOTSIE ROLL"

EACH SERVING Amount: 1 portion
Exchanges: 1 meat
                2 milk
                1/2 fat

Chol: 37 mg   Carbo: 50 gm   Fat: 4 gm
Calories: 298   Protein: 30 gm   Fiber: Tr.
Sodium: 546 mg

INGREDIENTS:

1/4 C. ricotta cheese

1/4 tsp. vanilla

2 pkgs. sugar substitute

2/3 C. non-fat dry powdered milk

1 Tbsp. cocoa

STEPS IN PREPARATION:

1. Cream together the first 3 ingredients. Add non-fat dry powdered milk, mix well and roll on waxed paper into cylinder approximately 6" long.
2. Wrap and chill.
3. Cut into pieces.

Serves 1

MOCK BABY RUTH

EACH SERVING Amount: 1 portion
Exchanges: 2 meat
1 bread
1 milk
2 fat

Chol: 6 mg   **Carbo:** 44 gm   **Fat:** 17 gm
Calories: 387 **Protein:** 22 gm **Fiber:** 7 gm
Sodium: 530 mg

INGREDIENTS:
3/4 C. grape nuts flakes
1/3 C. non-fat dry powdered milk
1 Tbsp. cocoa
2 Tbsp. peanut butter
1 pkg. sugar substitute
1 Tbsp. hot water
1 tsp. vanilla

STEPS IN PREPARATION:
Mix all ingredients well, shape into logs, and freeze.
Serves 1

FUDGE CANDY

EACH SERVING Amount: 2 pieces
Exchanges: 1/2 bread
1/2 fat

Chol: Tr. Carbo: 3 gm Fat: 1 gm
Calories: 28 Protein: 1 gm Fiber: Tr.
Sodium: 41 mg

INGREDIENTS:

1 (12 oz.) can evaporated skimmed milk
3 Tbsp. cocoa
1/4 C diet margarine
4 pkgs. sugar substitute
dash salt
1 tsp. vanilla extract
5 C. rice cereal, blended into crumbs (Measure 5
   cups cereal and then blend into crumbs.)
8 pkgs. sugar substitute
1/4 C. nuts (very finely chopped)

STEPS IN PREPARATION:

1. Combine milk and cocoa in saucepan; cook
   and beat over low heat until cocoa is dissolved.
   Add margarine, 4 pkgs sugar substitute, salt.
   Bring to a boil; reduce heat and cook for 5
   minutes.
2. Remove from heat; add cereal crumbs and
   vanilla. Cool 15 minutes. Add 8 pkgs. sugar
   substitute.
3. Divide in half; roll each half into a tube shape
   and roll in finely chopped nuts.
4. Wrap in waxed paper; chill overnight. Cut into
   32 slices.

Serves 16

CHOCOLATE LOG

EACH SERVING Amount: 1 portion
Exchanges: 2 meat   1 milk
                 1/4 bread   1/2 fat
                 1 fruit

Chol: 222 mg **Carbo:** 37 gm **Fat:** 6 gm
Calories: 289 **Protein:** 22 gm **Fiber:** 2 gm
Sodium: 535 mg

INGREDIENTS:

2 eggs
2 slices lite bread
1 (9 inch) banana
2/3 C. non-fat dry powdered milk
1 1/2 Tbsp. cocoa
1/2 tsp. cream of tartar
1/2 tsp. baking soda
1 tsp. vanilla
Filling:
   1/2 C. low-fat cottage cheese
   1 tsp. vanilla
   4 pkg. sugar substitute

STEPS IN PREPARATION:

1. Blend first eight ingredients until smooth. Pour onto cookie sheet that has been sprayed with non stick cooking spray. The cookie sheet should be 10 X 14.
2. Bake 10 minutes at 350 degrees. Remove; place on waxed paper. Let cool 10-15 minutes.
3. Cream together Filling ingredients (can use blender). Spread evenly over crust. Roll like jelly roll. Cut in half; chill or even freeze at least 1 hour.

Serves 2

SOFT SERVE ICE CREAM

EACH SERVING Amount: 1 portion
Exchanges: 1 milk
1/2 fruit

Chol: 5 mg   Carbo: 27 gm Fat: Tr.
Calories: 138 Protein: 10 gm Fiber: 2 gm
Sodium: 156 mg

INGREDIENTS:
1/3 C. non-fat dry powdered milk
1 C. frozen peaches
1 C. skim milk
1 C. ice cubes
1/2 tsp. vanilla

STEPS IN PREPARATION:
Blend in blender.
Serves 2

DOTTY'S DROPS

EACH SERVING Amount: 1 portion
Exchanges: 1 meat   1 fruit
1/2 milk   1 fat

Chol: 3 mg   Carbo: 24 gm Fat: 9 gm
Calories: 202 Protein: 11 gm Fiber: 3 gm
Sodium: 156 mg

INGREDIENTS:
2 Tbsp. peanut butter
3 oz. banana (mashed)
1/3 C. non-fat dry powdered milk
1 tsp. cocoa
1 to 2 Tbsp. hot water

STEPS IN PREPARATION:
Drop by spoonfuls onto waxed paper. Freeze.
Serves 2

MOUNDS BALLS

Chol: 10 mg   **Carbo:** 46 gm   **Fat:** 1 gm
Calories: 233 **Protein:** 16 gm **Fiber:** 1 gm
Sodium: 265 mg

INGREDIENTS:

1/3 C. non-fat dry powdered milk

1 Tbsp. cocoa

1/2 C. crushed pineapple, drained

1 Tbsp. pineapple juice

1 tsp. flaked coconut, unsweetened

1/2 tsp. vanilla

1/2 tsp. coconut extract

STEPS IN PREPARATION:

1. Mix all ingredients together well.
2. Drop by tablespoonfuls onto wax paper and freeze. (omit coconut - you can omit fat)

Serves 1

APPLE FRITTERS

INGREDIENTS:
1 apple, peeled and cored
1 egg
1 slice lite bread, crumbled
1/8 tsp. vanilla
1 Tbsp. water
2 pkg.sugar substitute
dash cinnamon
1 Tbsp. diet maragarine

STEPS IN PREPARATION:
1. Grate apple and set aside.
2. Combine all other ingredients in blender and beat until smooth. Fold in apple and mix well. Drop by tablespoons onto non-stick skillet.
3. Cook until lightly brown and throughly done.
4. Mix a drop of maple extract with your measured amount of diet margarine and melt over hot fritters.
Serves 1

BAKED APPLE

EACH SERVING Amount: 1 portion
Exchanges: 1 fruit
                   1/2 milk

Chol: 0   **Carbo:** 33 gm **Fat:** Tr.
Calories: 127 **Protein:** 6 gm **Fiber:** 3 gm
Sodium: 86 mg

INGREDIENTS:

1 Rome apple (If using Delicious apple, peel skin, or else it will be tough).

STEPS IN PREPARATION:

1. Put apple into dish containing 2 Tbsp. water. Sprinkle top of apple with cinnamon and 1 pkg. sugar substitute.
2. Bake at 350 degrees for about 20 minutes, or microwave on high for about 5 minutes.
3. Mix 1/2 C. low-fat yogurt, 2-3 pkgs. sugar substitute, and 1/2 tsp. vanilla. Pour over apple and eat!

Serves 1

CRUSTY BAKED APPLES

INGREDIENTS:

6 tart apples, cored
3 Tbsp. diet margarine
2 Tbsp. flour
2 tsp. brown sugar substitute
1/2 tsp. vanilla

STEPS IN PREPARATION:

1. Pare apples halfway down. Put pared side up into baking dish.
2. Melt margarine. Stir in flour and mix well. Add brown sugar substitute and vanilla. Spread over apples.
3. Bake at 425 degrees until crust is set, about 10 minutes. Lower temperature to 350 degrees. Bake until apples are tender.

Serves 6

APPLESAUCE COOKIES

EACH SERVING Amount: 3 pieces
Exchanges: 1 bread
1/2 fruit
1/2 fat

Chol: 8 mg   **Carbo:** 27 gm **Fat:** 4 gm
Calories: 157 **Protein:** 4 gm **Fiber:** 2 gm
Sodium: 241 mg

INGREDIENTS:
1/4 C. diet margarine, soft
2 Tbsp. brown sugar substitute
1 egg
1 tsp. vanilla
1/2 C. unsweetened applesauce
1 C. flour
1 tsp. soda
1 tsp. cinnamon
1/4 tsp. salt
1/8 tsp. cloves
1/2 C. rolled oats
1/2 C. raisins or chopped dates

STEPS IN PREPARATION:
1. Cream margarine with sugar substitute. Add egg and beat until light. Blend in vanilla and applesauce.
2. Stir flour, soda, spices, oats and raisins together. Add to creamed mixture. Blend well.
3. Drop by spoonfuls onto cookie sheet that has been sprayed with non-stick cooking spray and bake at 375 degrees for 10 minutes.
Yields 24

PUMPKIN COOKIES

EACH SERVING Amount: 2 pieces
Exchanges: 1/2 bread
1/4 fruit
1/2 fat

Chol: 8 mg   Carbo: 15 gm   Fat: 5 gm
Calories: 111   Protein: 2 gm   Fiber: 1 gm
Sodium: 175 mg

INGREDIENTS:

1/4 C. vegetable oil
12 pkgs. sugar substitute
1 egg beaten
1 C. canned or fresh cooked pumpkin
1 C. sifted flour
2 tsp. baking powder
1/2 tsp. salt
1 1/4 tsp. cinnamon
1/2 tsp. nutmeg
1/8 tsp. ginger
1/2 C. raisins

STEPS IN PREPARATION:

1. Combine oil and add sugar substitute gradually. Cream until light and fluffy. Add egg and pumpkin; mix well.
2. Sift flour, baking powder, salt and spices together. Stir into pumpkin mixture. Add raisins.
3. Drop by teaspoonfuls onto cookie sheet sprayed wiht non-stick spray. Bake at 350 degrees for 25 minutes.

Yields 24

TOASTY OATMEAL COOKIES

EACH SERVING Amount: 3 pieces
Exchanges: 1/2 meat
1 bread
1/2 fruit
1 fat

Chol: 8 mg   **Carbo:** 23 gm   **Fat:** 7 gm
Calories: 172   **Protein:** 8 gm   **Fiber:** 3 gm
Sodium: 47 mg

INGREDIENTS:
2 C. quick oatmeal, lightly toasted
1 (9 inch) peeled very ripe banana, mashed
4 Tbsp. nutty peanut butter
1 egg
1 tsp. vanilla
2 pkg. sugar substitute

STEPS IN PREPARATION:
1. Spread oatmeal onto cookie sheet, place in 350 degree oven about 15-20 minutes, until lightly toasted, stirring occasionally.
2. Blend banana, peanut butter, egg, vanilla and sugar substitute with mixer until well blended. Stir in oatmeal. Let mixture set a minute.
3. Use 2 cookie sheets that have been sprayed with non-stick spray. Drop mixture by 24 rounded tablespoons, try to divide evenly. Flatten slightly with fingers or back of spoon.
4. Bake at 350 degrees for about 12 minutes until lightly browned.

Yields 24

APPLE-PUMPKIN COOKIES

EACH SERVING Amount: 1 portion
Exchanges: 1 bread
1 fruit
1 milk

Chol: 8 mg   **Carbo:** 60 gm **Fat:** 1 gm
Calories: 248 **Protein:** 16 gm **Fiber:** 5 gm
Sodium: 223 mg

INGREDIENTS:

4 oz. canned or fresh cooked pumpkin
1/3 C. non-fat dry powdered milk
1 apple, grated
3 pkg. sugar substitute
1 1/2 tsp. cinnamon
dash nutmeg

STEPS IN PREPARATION:

Mix all ingredients and drop batter by tablespoonfuls on cookie sheet, bake at 350 degrees for 15-20 minutes.
Yields 6

PINEAPPLE COOKIES

EACH SERVING Amount: 3 pieces
Exchanges: 1 1/4 bread
1 fruit

Chol: 0   **Carbo:** 30 gm   **Fat:** 1 gm
Calories: 131 **Protein:** 4 gm **Fiber:** 3 gm
Sodium: 65 mg

INGREDIENTS:

2 C. whole wheat flour
1 (6 oz.) can concentrated pineapple juice
(unsweetned)
3/4 tsp. baking soda
1/4 C. powder butter flavoring made into liquid
(We used Butter Buds. Follow recipe on box for
making into liquid.)
1/2 tsp. almond extract
1/4 C. chopped dates
1/2 C. drained crushed pineapple (in own juice)
1 Tbsp. unsweetened coconut, optional

STEPS IN PREPARATION:

1. Preheat oven to 350 degrees.
2. Spray cookie sheet with non-stick spray.
3. Mix all ingredients well (mixture will be stiff).
4. Drop by spoonful evenly to make 30 cookies
   to cookie sheet. Press gently with spoon to
   flatten.

Yields 30

RAISIN SCONES

EACH SERVING Amount: 1 piece
Exchanges: 1/2 bread
1/2 fruit
1/2 fat

Chol: 18 mg **Carbo:** 18 gm **Fat:** 5 gm
Calories: 119 **Protein:** 2 gm **Fiber:** 1 gm
Sodium: 298 mg

INGREDIENTS:

1 C. flour
3 pkg. sugar substitute
2 tsp. baking powder
1/2 tsp. baking soda
1/2 tsp. salt
1/2 tsp. ground nutmeg
1/2 C. diet margarine
1 C. raisins
3/4 C. low-fat buttermilk
1 egg white, lightly beaten, for glaze

STEPS IN PREPARATION:

1. In large bowl, combine flour, sugar substitute, baking powder, soda, salt and nutmeg. Cut in margarine until mixture resembles coarse meal. Mix in raisins, then mix in buttermilk with fork.
2. Gather dough into ball and knead on lightly floured board about 2 minutes. Roll or pat dough out 3/4 inch thick.
3. With sharp knife, cut dough into 3-inch triangles.

4. Space dough triangles apart on baking sheet sprayed with non-stick cooking spray. Brush tops with egg white.
5. Bake in preheated oven at 425 degrees about 15 minutes or until nicely browned. You may want to sprinkle with sugar substitute after cooking. Serve warm with diet margarine or diet jelly.

Serves 12

"SUGAR & SPICE" POPCORN

EACH SERVING Amount: 3 cups
Exchanges: 1 bread
1 fat

Chol: 0 **Carbo:** 15 gm **Fat:** 7 gm
Calories: 156 **Protein:** 2 gm **Fiber:** 3 gm
Sodium: 926 mg

INGREDIENTS:
9 C. popped corn cooked without oil
3 Tbsp. diet margarine
1 to 2 pkg. sugar substitute
1/4 tsp. cinnamon
1/4 tsp. nutmeg

STEPS IN PREPARATION:
1. Melt margarine, add sugar substitute and spices.
2. Pour mixture over popped corn, stirring well.

Serves 3

POPCORN TREAT

EACH SERVING Amount: 3 cups
Exchanges: 1 bread

Chol: 0   **Carbo:** 14 gm   **Fat:** 1 gm
Calories: 117   **Protein:** 2 gm   **Fiber:** 3 gm
Sodium: 816 mg

Spray fresh popped popcorn with butter flavored non-stick cooking spray. Sprinkle onto it sugar-free gelatin or mexican seasoning.

APPLESTICK SNACK

EACH SERVING Amount: 1 portion
Exchanges: 1/2 fruit

Chol: 0   Carbo: 9 gm   Fat: Tr.
Calories: 42   Protein: 1 gm   Fiber: 1 gm
Sodium: 51 mg

INGREDIENTS:

1 small pkg. sugar-free gelatin, any flavor
3/4 C. boiling water
1/2 C. apple juice
Ice cubes
1 medium unpeeled apple, cut into matchstick
pieces

STEPS IN PREPARATION:

1. Dissolve gelatin in boiling water.
2. Combine juice and ice cubes to make 1 1/4 cups. Add to gelatin and stir until slightly thickened; remove any unmelted ice. Add apple.
3. Chill in bowl or individual dishes until set, about 2 hours.

Serves 4

ROSY APPLE SNACK

EACH SERVING Amount: 1 portion
Exchanges: 1 fruit

Chol: 0   **Carbo:** 19 gm **Fat:** Tr.
Calories: 87   **Protein:** 2 gm **Fiber:** 1 gm
Sodium: 103 mg

INGREDIENTS:

1 small pkg. sugar-free gelatin, raspberry
3/4 C. boiling water
11/3 C. unsweetened applesauce
1 tsp. lemon juice

STEPS IN PREPARATION:

1. Dissolve gelatin in boiling water. Add applesauce and lemon juice; mix well.
2. Pour into bowl or individual dishes and chill until set, about 2 hours.

Serves 2

FOAMY PEACH SNACK

EACH SERVING **Amount:** 1 portion
Exchanges: 1/2 fruit

Chol: 0   **Carbo:** 4 gm   **Fat:** 0
Calories: 22   **Protein:** 1 gm   **Fiber:** 1 gm
Sodium: 37 mg

INGREDIENTS:

1 (8 oz.) can sliced peaches, in own juice
1 small pkg. sugar-free gelatin, any flavor
1 1/2 C. ice cubes

STEPS IN PREPARATION:

1. Drain peaches, reserving juice. Add water to juice to make 3/4 cup; bring measured liquid to a boil.
2. Pour boiling liquid into blender container. Add gelatin and blend at high speed until dissolved, about 1 minute. Add ice cubes and stir until ice is partially melted. Add peaches and blend at high speed until ice is melted, about 2 minutes.
3. Chill until set; about 2 hours.

Serves 6

TERMS & CHARTS

SUGAR

A number of terms may appear on food labels to indicate that a product contains sugar. Knowing these terms will help you identify the ingredients that need to be calculated into a meal plan. The following list identifies these terms.

SUGAR TERMS:

Brown Sugar:	a soft sugar in which crystals are covered by a film of refined dark syrup.
Carbohydrate:	a nutrient made up of sugars and starches.
Corn Sugar:	a sugar made by the beakdown of cornstarch
Corn Syrup:	a syrup containing several different sugars that is obtained by the partial breakdown of corn-starch
Dextrin:	a sugar formed by the partial breakdown of starch
Dextrose:	another name for sugar
Fructose:	the simple sugar found in fruit, juices and honey
Galactose:	a type of simple sugar found in lactose (milk sugar)
Glucose:	a type of simple sugar found in the blood, derived from food, and used by the body for heat and energy
Honey:	a sweet, thick material made in the honey sac of various bees
Invert Sugar:	a combination of sugars found in fruits
Lactose:	the sugar found in miik
Levulose:	another name for fruit sugar
Maltose:	a crystalline sugar formed by the breakdown of starch
Mannitol:	a sugar alcohol
Mannose:	a sugar from manna and the ivory nut
Maple Sugar:	a syrup made by concentrating the sap of the sugar maple
Molasses:	the thick syrup separated from raw sugar in manufacturing process of sugar
Sorbitol:	a sugar alcohol
Sorghum:	a syrup from the juice of the sorghum grain

Starch:	a powdery complex chain of sugars; for example, cornstarch
Sucrose:	another name for table sugar
Sugar:	a carbohydrate, including the monosaccharides; fructose, galactose, and glucose and the disaccharides; sucrose, maltose, and lactose
Xylose:	a wood sugar found in corn cobs, straw, bran woodgum, the bran of seeds, cherries, pears, peaches, and plums
Xylotol:	a sugar alcohol

TERMS USED

CALORIE - a unit of heat that measures the amount of energy in food.

CARBOHYDRATE - a major nutrient found in sugars, breads, cereals, vegetables, fruit, and milk; provides 4 calories per gram weight.

CHOLESTEROL - a fat-like substance which is made in the liver and found in animal foods.

DIETETIC FOODS - foods prepared for special diets, such as low-fat, low-sodium, sugar-free, calorie-reduced and low-cholesterol.

DIGESTION - the breakdown of foods in the disgestive tract into simple substances the body can use for energy and nourishment.

ENRICHED FOODS - foods made from refined grains to which one or more nutrients have been added to increase the nutrient value.

FAT - a major nutrient found in meats, eggs, milk and milk products, oils, margarine, salad dressings, and nuts which provides 9 calories per gram weight.

FIBER - that part of food which is not digested and adds bulk but no calories to the diet.

FOOD EXCHANGE - a group of foods which contain similar nutrients.

FREE FOODS - foods which have few calories and carbohydrates and do not need to be counted as Exchanges.

GRAM - a unit of weight in the metric system; one ounce equals 28.25 grams.

MEAL PLAN - a guide used to show the number of Exchanges to eat at each meal.

MINERALS - a group of nutrients necessary for life found in small amounts in foods.

MONOUNSATURATED FAT - a neutral fat which does not increase or decrease serum (blood) cholesterol levels.

NUTRIENT - a substance necessary for life and found in food.

NUTRITION - the process by which the body uses food to nourish cells.

POLYUNSATURATED FAT - a fat found in plants which tends to lower serum (blood) cholesterol levels.

PROTEIN - a major nutrient which is essential for life and needed for building and repairing body cells and which is found in meats, eggs, milk and milk products. Proteins provide 4 calories per gram weight.

SATURATED FAT - a fat which tends to raise serum (blood) cholesterol level and is usually found in solid fat.

STARCH - a complex form of carbohydrate which is changed to sugar during digestion.

TRYGLYCERIDES - a fat normally present in the blood, made from food which may be affected by excess weight, a high fat diet, alcohol, and sugar.

VITAMIN - a nutrient necessary for life found in small amounts in foods.

COOKING TERMS

BAKE - Cook in an oven or oven-like appliance. Always bake a dish uncovered unless recipe specifies otherwise.

BASTE - Brush or spoon a glaze, a sauce, or drippings over a food as it cooks to add flavor and to help keep the surface moist.

BEAT - Use a brisk up-and-over motion to add air to a mixture and make it smooth. Or, use an electric mixer or rotary beater to achieve similar results.

BLANCH - Briefly boil or steam a food to prevent spoilage during freezing, or to loosen skins for peeling.

BLEND - Process a food in an electric blender to mix, chop, or puree. Or combine by hand with a stirring motion to make a uniform mixture.

BOIL - Cook in liquid that is heated until bubbles rise to the surface and break. In a full rolling boil, bubbles form rapidly throughout the mixture.

BRAISE - Cook slowly with a small amount of liquid in a covered pan on the range top or in the oven.

BROIL - Cook by direct heat under a broiler in an electric or gas range.

CHILL - Refrigerate to reduce temperature of a food.

CHOP - Cut into small irregular-shaped pieces.

COOL - Let stand at room temperature to reduce the temperature of a food. When a recipe says, "cool quickly," the food should be refrigerated or set in a bowl of ice water to quickly reduce its temperature.

CREAM - Beat with a spoon or electric mixer to make mixture light and fluffy.

CUBE - Cut into pieces that are the same size on each side - at least 1/2 inch.

DICE - Cut into cubes that are 1/8 to 1/4 inch on each side.

DISSOLVE - Stir a dry ingredient into a liquid until the dry ingredient is no longer visible.

FILLET - Cut lean meat or fish into pieces without a bone.

FLAKE - Gently break into small pieces.

FOLD - Gently combine two or more ingredients.

GARNISH - Decorate a food, usually with another food.

GRATE - Rub across a grater to break a food into fine particles.

GRILL - Cook over hot coals.

GRIND - Use a food grinder to cut a food into very fine pieces.

KNEAD - Work dough with the hands in a pressing, folding, and turning motion.

MARINATE - Allow a food to stand in a liquid that adds flavor to the food.

MINCE - Cut into very tiny, irregular-shaped pieces.

MIX - Combine ingredients by stirring.

PARTIALLY SET - A term used to describe gelatin mixtures at the point in setting when the consistency resembles raw egg whites.

PIT - Remove the seed from a piece of fruit.

POACH - Cook in a hot liquid, being careful that the food holds its shape.

PUREE - Use a blender, food processor, or food mill to convert a food into a liquid or heavy paste.

REDUCE - Boil rapidly to evaporate liquid so mixture becomes thicker.

ROAST - Cook a meat, uncovered, in the oven. "Pot roasting" refers to braising a meat roast.

SAUTE - Cook in a small amount of butter, margarine, oil, cooking spray or shortening.

SCALD - Bring to a temperature just below boiling so that tiny bubbles form at the edges of the pan.

SCORE - Cut shallow grooves or slits through the outer layer of a food.

SEAR - Brown surface of meat quickly with intense heat.

SHRED - Rub on a shredder to form long, narrow pieces.

SIFT - Pass flour or a dry mixture through a sieve or sifter to incorporate air and break up lumps.

SIMMER - Cook in liquid that is just below the boiling point. Bubbles burst before reaching the surface.

STEAM - Cook using steam, sometimes under pressure.

STEEP - Extract the flavor or color from a substance by letting it stand in hot liquid.

STEW - Cook slowly in simmering liquid.

STIR - Use a spoon to combine ingredients with a circular or figure-8 motion.

STIR-FRY - Cook quickly in a small amount of hot fat, stirring constantly.

TOSS - Mix ingredients lightly by lifting and dropping with a spoon, or a spoon and a fork.

WHIP - Beat lightly and rapidly, incorporating air into a mixture to make it light and to increase its volume.

INGREDIENT EQUIVALENTS

Food	Amount Before Preparation	Approximate Measure After Preparation
CEREALS		
Macaroni	1 cup (3-1/2 oz.)	2-1/2 cups cooked
Noodles	3 cups (4 oz.)	3 cups cooked
Spaghetti	8 oz.	4 cups cooked
Long grain rice	1 cup (7 oz.)	3 cups cooked
Quick-cooking rice	1 cup (3 oz.)	2 cups cooked
Popcorn	1/4 cup	5 cups popped
CRUMBS		
Bread	1 slice	3/4 c. soft or 1/4 cup fine dry crumbs
Saltine crackers	28 squares	1 cup finely crushed
FRUITS		
Apples	1 medium	1 cup sliced
Apricots	1 medium	1/4 cup sliced
Avocados	1 medium	1-1/4 cups sliced
Bananas	1 medium	1/3 cup mashed
Cherries, red	1 pound	2 cups pitted
Grapes	1 pound	2-1/2 cups seeded
Lemons	1 medium	3 tablespoons juice 2 teaspoons peel
Limes	1 medium	2 tablespoons juice 1-1/2 teaspoons peel
Oranges	1 medium	1/4 to 1/3 cup juice 4 teaspoons peel
Peaches, Pears	1 medium	1/2 cup sliced
Rhubarb	1 pound (4 cups)	2 cups cooked
Strawberries	4 cups whole	4 cups sliced
VEGETABLES		
Beans and peas, dried	1 pound (2-1/2 cups)	6 cups cooked
Cabbage	1 pound (1 small)	5 cups shredded
Carrots, without tops	1 pound (6 medium)	3 cups shredded or 2-1/2 cups diced
Celery	1 medium bunch	4-1/2 cups chopped
Corn	1 medium ear	1/2 cup cut from cob
Green beans	1 pound (3 cups)	2-1/2 cups cooked
Green onions	1 bunch (7)	1/2 cup sliced
Green peppers	1 large	1 cup diced
Mushrooms	1 pound (6 cups)	6 cups sliced or 2 cups cooked
Onions	1 medium	1/2 cup chopped
Potatoes	1 medium	2/3 cup cubed or 1/2 cup mashed
Radishes	1 bunch	1 cup sliced
Spinach	1 pound (12 cups)	1-1/2 cups cooked
Tomatoes	1 medium	1/2 cup cooked
Zucchini	1 medium	1 cup sliced

EMERGENCY SUBSTITUTIONS

For best results, use ingredients specified in the recipe, since substitutions often change flavor and texture. When you are in a bind, use this chart to find an acceptable substitute.

IF YOU DON'T HAVE:	SUBSTITUTE:
1 tablespoon cornstarch(for thickening)	2 tablespoons all-purpose flour
1 teaspoon baking powder	1/4 teaspoon baking soda plus 1/2 cup buttermilk or sour milk (to replace 1/2 cup of liquid called for)
1 package active dry yeast	1 cake compressed yeast
1 square (1 oz) unsweetened chocolate	3 tablespoons unsweetened cocoa powder plus 1 tablespoon margarine
1 cup whipping cream, whipped	2 cups low calorie whipped dessert topping
1 cup sour milk or buttermilk	1 tablespoon lemon juice or vinegar plus enough milk to make 1 cup (let stand 5 minutes before using) or 1 cup milk plus 1-3/4 teaspoons cream of tartar
1 cup buttermilk	1 cup plain yogurt
1 cup milk	1 cup reconstituted nonfat dry milk
2 cups tomato sauce	3/4 cup tomato paste plus 1 cup water
1 cup tomato juice	1/2 cup tomato sauce plus 1 cup water
1 clove garlic	1/8 teaspoon garlic powder or minced dried garlic
1 small onion	1 teaspoon onion powder or 1 tablespoon minced dried onion rehydrated
1 teaspoon dry mustard	1 tablespoon prepared mustard
1 teaspoon finely shredded lemon peel	1/2 teaspoon lemon extract

MAKING FOOD ATTRACTIVE

A colorful garnish can make the difference between an everday meal and a festive occasion. For main dishes and vegetables, add interest with snipped parsley, sliced green onions, wedges of tomatoes or hard-cooked eggs, or whole or sliced mushrooms or cherry tomatoes.

Radish Roses: Cut tip off radish. Make 4 or 5 petals around the radish by cutting thin slices from top to -- but not through -- bottom of radish. Leave a little red between the petals. Chill in ice water till petals spread open. Drain before serving.

Scored Cucumbers: Run tines of fork lengthwise down cucumber, pressing to break through peel. Repeat at regular intervals around cucumber. Slice crosswise or on the bias.

Pickle Fans: Make 3 or 4 lengthwise slices from one end almost to the other. Spread slices apart to resemble a fan; press uncut end to hold in place.

Carrot Curls and Zigzags: With a vegetable peeler, shave thin, wide strips from a carrot. Roll up each strip; secure with a wooden pick. Or, make zigzags by threading carrot strips on picks accordian-style. Place curls or zigzags in ice water to crisp. Remove picks before serving.

Celery or Green Onion Brushes: Trim ends from celery stalks or green onions. At one or both ends, cut several lengthwise gashes about 2 inches long. Place stalks in ice water to crisp. Drain well before serving.

WEIGHTS AND MEASURES

3 teaspoons = 1 tablespoon
4 tablespoons = 1/4 cup
5-1/3 tablespoons = 1/3 cup
8 tablespoons = 1/2 cup
10-1/2 tablespoons = 2/3 cup
12 tablespoons = 3/4 cup
16 tablespoons = 1 cup
1 ounce = 28.35 grams
1 gram = 0.035 ounces
1 cup = 8 fluid ounces
1 cup = 1/2 pint
2 cups = 1 pint
4 cups = 1 quart
4 quarts = 1 gallon
8 quarts = 1 peck
4 pecks = 1 bushel
1 quart = 946.4 mililiters
1 liter = 1.06 quarts

Table of Equivalents for Sugar Substitutes

BRAND NAME	SUBSTITUTION FOR SUGAR	BRAND NAME	SUBSTITUTION FOR SUGAR
Adolph's (powder)		**Sucaryl (liquid)**	
2 shakes of jar	= 1 rounded teaspoon sugar	1/8 teaspoon	= 1 teaspoon sugar
1/4 teaspoon	= 1 tablespoon sugar	1/3 teaspoon	= 1 tablespoon sugar
1 teaspoon	= 1/4 cup sugar	1/2 teaspoon	= 4 teaspoons sugar
2-1/2 teaspoons	= 2/3 cup sugar	1-1/2 teaspoons	= 1/4 cup sugar
1 tablespoon	= 3/4 cup sugar	1 tablespoon	= 1/2 cup sugar
4 teaspoons	= 1 cup sugar		
		Superose (liquid)	
Equal (powder)*		4 drops	= 1 teaspoon sugar
1 packet	= 2 teaspoons sugar	1/8 teaspoon	= 2 teaspoons sugar
		1/8 teaspoon plus	
Fasweet (liquid)		4 drops	= 1 tablespoon sugar
1/8 teaspoon	= 1 teaspoon sugar	1-1/2 teaspoons	= 1/2 cup sugar
1/4 teaspoon	= 2 teaspoons sugar	1 tablespoon	= 1 cup sugar
1/3 teaspoon	= 1 tablespoon sugar		
1 tablespoon	= 1/2 cup sugar	**Sugar Twin (powder)**	
2 tablespoons	= 1 cup sugar	1 teaspoon	= 1 teaspoon sugar
		Sugar Twin, Brown (powder)	
		1 teaspoon	= 1 teaspoon brown sugar

*Use only after cooking or in uncooked dishes

Sugar equivalents for various brand names of sugar substitutes are listed for your convenience only and not as as endorsement.

299

Table of Equivalents for Sugar Substitutes

BRAND NAME	SUBSTITUTION FOR SUGAR	BRAND NAME	SUBSTITUTION FOR SUGAR
Sweet N' Low (powder)		**Sweet One (powder)**	
1/10 teaspoon	= 1 teaspoon sugar	1 packet	= 2 teaspoons sugar
1 packet	= 2 teaspoons sugar	3 packets	= 1/4 cup sugar
1/3 teaspoon	= 1 tablespoon sugar	4 packets	= 1/3 cup sugar
1 teaspoon	= 1/4 cup sugar	6 packets	= 1/2 cup sugar
1-1/4 teaspoons	= 1/3 cup sugar	12 packets	= 1 cup sugar
2 teaspoons	= 1/2 cup sugar		
4 teaspoons	= 1 cup sugar	**Sweet-10 (liquid)**	
		10 drops	= 1 teaspoon sugar
Sweet N' Low, Brown (powder)		1/2 teaspoon	= 4 teaspoons sugar
1/4 teaspoon	= 1 tablespoon sugar	1-1/2 teaspoon	= 1/4 cup sugar
1 teaspoon	= 1/4 cup sugar	1 tablespoon	= 1/2 cup sugar
1-1/3 teaspoons	= 1/3 cup	2 tablespoons	= 1 cup sugar
2 teaspoons	= 1/2 cup sugar		
4 teaspoons	= 1 cup sugar	**Zero -Cal (liquid)**	
		10 drops	= 1 teaspoon sugar
Sweet'ner (powder)		30 drops	= 1 tablespoon sugar
1 packet	= 2 teaspoons sugar	3/4 teaspoon	= 2 tablespoons sugar
		1 tablespoon	= 1/2 cup sugar
Sweet Magic (powder)		2 tablespoons	= 1 cup sugar
1 packet	= 2 teaspoons sugar		

Sugar equivalents for various brand names of sugar substitutes are listed for your convenience only and not as as endorsement.

Spice and Herb Chart

SPICE OR HERBS	MEAT, FISH AND POULTRY	VEGETABLES AND PASTA	SALADS	EGGS AND CHEESE
Basil	Lamb, Pork, Liver, Veal, Fish Fillets, Shrimp, Tuna, Duck, Chicken, Venison, Turkey	Peas, Eggplant, Green Beans, Cauliflower, Squash, Tomatoes, Onions, Soups	Egg, Seafood, Tossed Green, Tomato, Chicken, Cucumber	Scrambled Eggs, Omelets, Cheese Sauce
Bay Leaves	Stews, Pot Roast, Tripe, Fish, Tongue, Corned Beef	Beets, Carrots, Stewed Tomatoes, Boiled Potatoes, Soups	Aspic, Fish	
Black Pepper	Steaks, Chops, Roast, Stews, Chicken, Game, Casseroles	Green Beans, Squash, Beets, Spinach, Peas	Tossed Green, Potato, Pickled Beets, Bean	
Cloves	Baked Ham, Stews, Pot Roast, Spiced Tongue, Game Stews, Venison, Roast Chicken	Winter Squash, Onions, Tomatoes, Sweet Potatoes	Spiced Apple, Spiced Peach	
Oregano	Ground Beef, Pork, Lamb, Meat Loaf, Chicken, Guinea Hen, Shrimp, Lobster, Liver	Tomatoes, Cabbage, Lentils, Broccoli, Soups, Onions	Tomato Aspic, Fish, Cucumber, Bean, Potato	Souffles, Omelets, Cheese Sauce, Scrambled Eggs

301

Spice and Herb Chart

SPICE OR HERBS	MEAT, FISH AND POULTRY	VEGETABLES AND PASTA	SALADS	EGGS AND CHEESE
Paprika	Beef, Stew, Fish, Lobster, Chicken, Fish Chowder, Casseroles	Potato, Corn, Rice, Casseroles, Noodles	Potato, Macaroni, Chicken, Tuna	Deviled Eggs, Creamed Eggs, Cheese Sauce,
Red Pepper	Stews, Italian Dishes, Chicken, Seafood, Creole, Fish, Casseroles	Casseroles	Seafood, Chicken, Turkey	Cheese Sauce, Omelets
Sage	Cottage Cheese, Stews, Pork, Lamb, Goose, Turkey, Rabbit, Fish, Chcken, Duck	Lima Beans, Eggplant, Onions, Tomatoes, Soups, Carrots	Tomato, Tossed Green, Bean	Cottage Cheese, Creamed Eggs, Souffles
Thyme	Fish Fillets, Lamb, Beef, Meat Loaf, Stews, Liver, Chicken, Venison, Scallops, Turkey	Beets, Onions, Carrots, Brussel Sprouts, Zucchini, Asparagus	Pickled Beets, Tomato, Aspic, Cole Slaw, Chicken	Deviled Eggs, Souffles, Omelets, Cottage Cheese
White Pepper	Stew, Veal, Fish, Casseroles	Caulifower, Cabbage, Rice, Asparagus, Potatoes	Salmon, Tomato, Tuna, Shrimp, Chicken, Turkey	Deviled Eggs, Cheese Sauce, Creamed Eggs,

NUTRIENT	FUNCTIONS IN YOUR BODY	MAJOR FOOD SOURCES
Carbohydrates	Supply energy. Help body use other nutrients.	Cereals, fruits, vegetables, breads, sugars, milk, honey, cakes, cookies, pies, pasta.
Fats	Supply energy. Help maintain body temperature. Transport fat-soluble vitamins.	Margarine, butter, oils, shortening, cream, nuts, bacon, olives, whole milk.
Proteins	Build and repair body tissues. Help balance body chemicals.	Meat, poultry, fish, milk, cheese, nuts, dried peas and beans.
Vitamins Vitamin A	Helps eyes adjust to dim light. Helps keep skin healthy. Helps resist infection. Helps bones grow.	Liver, butter, cream, whole milk, egg yolk, broccoli, collards, spinach, carrots, sweet potatoes, pumpkin, winter squash, apricots cantaloupe, greens.
Vitamin C	Helps hold body cells together. Helps heal wounds. Helps build bones and teeth. Helps absorb iron.	Oranges, grapefruit, cantaloupe, strawberries raw cabbage, tomatoes, broccoli, green pepper.
Vitamin D	Helps body use calcium and phosphorous.	Liver, fortified milk, egg yolk (exposure to sunlight produces vitamin D in the skin.)
Vitamin E	Helps keep blood cells intact. Helps keep body fats intact.	Wheat germ, polyunsaturated vegetable oils.

Nutrient Chart

NUTRIENT	FUNCTIONS IN YOUR BODY	MAJOR FOOD SOURCES
Vitamin K	Is necessary for clotting blood.	Liver, spinach, greens, cabbage, cauliflower
Thiamin (B1)	Helps body get energy from food. Helps keep nervous system healthy. Promotes good appetite and digestion.	Liver and other organ meats, meats, especially pork, poultry, whole-grain and enriched breads and cereals, nuts, dried peas and beans.
Riboflavin (B2)	Helps body get energy from food. Promotes healthy skin, eyes, and clear vision.	Milk, organ meats, egg white, enriched breads and cereals.
Niacin	Helps body produce energy. Aids digestion and good appetite. Helps keep skin, tongue, nervous system, and digestive tract healthy.	Lean meat, fish, poultry, liver, peanuts, whole-grain and enriched breads and cereals.
Cobalamine (B12)	Helps build red blood cells. Promotes healthy nervous system.	Liver and other organ meats, meat, fish, poultry
Pyridoxine (B6)	Helps body use food. Helps build blood cells.	Egg yolk, whole-grain cereals, liver, peanuts, soybeans.
Minerals Calcium	Builds bones and teeth. Helps clot blood. Helps nerves, muscles, and heart to function well.	Milk, cheese, yogurt, buttermilk, tofu.
Phosphorous	Builds bones and teeth. Helps body get energy from food.	Milk and milk products, meat, fish, poultry, eggs nuts, dried peas and beans.

NUTRIENT	FUNCTIONS IN YOUR BODY	MAJOR FOOD SOURCES
Minerals Iron	Forms part of red blood cells. Helps body get energy from blood.	Liver and other organ meats, egg yolk, meat, poultry, oysters, enriched and whole-grain breads and cereals, dried peas and beans.
Sodium	Helps control water balance. Regulates nerve impulses and muscle contractions.	Salt, meat, fish, poultry, milk and milk products, eggs
Potassium	Helps control water balance. Regulates nerve impulses, muscle contractions, and heart rhythm.	Fruits, vegetables, meat, fish, poultry, milk and milk products.
Iodine	Regulates energy.	Seafood, iodized salt.
Magnesium	Is part of bones and teeth. Helps body use carbohydrates. Helps regulate nerve and muscle contractions.	Whole-grain cereals, nuts, dried peas and beans, milk, meat, leafy green vegetables
Copper	Helps form red blood cells. Aids absorption and use of iron. Helps body get energy from food.	Liver, shellfish, meat, nuts, dried peas and beans, whole-grain cereals.
Water	Helps build and bathe body cells. Aids digestion and absorption. Helps lubricate joints and organs. Regulates body temperature.	All liquids such as water, coffee, tea, soft drinks, fruit and vegetable juices, milk, ice.

Index

BREAKFAST

DESSERTS

EGG & CHEESE

FISH

SALADS

SOUPS

VEGETABLES